BIRDS OF PREY
AND RED GROUSE

*S M Redpath[1] and S J Thirgood[2]**

Edited by I Newton[3]

[1] *Institute of Terrestrial Ecology, Hill of Brathens, Banchory,*
  Kincardineshire AB31 4BY
[2] *The Game Conservancy Trust, Crubenmore Lodge, Newtonmore,*
  Inverness-shire PH20 1BE
[3] *Institute of Terrestrial Ecology, Monks Wood, Abbots Ripton,*
  Huntingdon, Cambs PE17 2LS
* *The order of authorship was decided on the toss of a coin*

Research sponsored by:
The Buccleuch Estates
Peter Buckley of Westerhall Estate
The Game Conservancy Trust
The Game Conservancy Scottish Research Trust
Institute of Terrestrial Ecology (NERC)
Joint Nature Conservation Committee
Royal Society for the Protection of Birds
Scottish Natural Heritage

Centre for Ecology and Hydrology

Natural Environment Research Council

London: The Stationery Office

Contents

Foreword

One of the most topical issues in upland land management concerns the relationship between birds of prey and red grouse. Birds of prey are of great conservation interest, while grouse are important to the economy of many upland estates. The persecution of birds of prey, which stems from concerns about their impact on viable moorland management, has generated conflict between conservation and grouse shooting interests. This is all the more regrettable, given the shared concerns that both sides have for the future of heather moorland.

So far, debate on the raptor/grouse issue has been marked by a wealth of strongly held opinion, but by a distinct shortage of scientifically based information relevant to current conditions. It was for this reason that the present study was started. Its aim was to provide an assessment of the impact of raptors on the numbers and bags of grouse over a five-year period. The study was centred at Langholm, in the Scottish Borders, on land belonging to the Buccleuch Estates. The area had been managed as a high-quality grouse moor since the last century, and until the start of the study the annual bags had tended to fluctuate, with peaks every six years or so. Additional studies were made on several other moors, distributed through northern England and Scotland, whose owners collaborated in various ways, including the provision of bag records. These supplementary data helped in the interpretation of findings from Langholm and also in assessing the applicability of the Langholm findings to other areas. On most of the moors concerned, as on many other moors, grouse bags had been declining for several decades.

The research was very much a collaborative venture, undertaken jointly by the Game Conservancy Trust and the Institute of Terrestrial Ecology, but funded and guided throughout by a consortium of interest groups that also included the Royal Society for the Protection of Birds, Scottish Natural Heritage, the Joint Nature Conservation Committee, the Game Conservancy Scottish Research Trust, the Buccleuch Estates and Peter Buckley of Westerhall Estate. In addition, the study benefitted greatly from previous research on red grouse, undertaken by the Game Conservancy Trust (mainly Dr P Hudson) and the Institute of Terrestrial Ecology (mainly Drs D Jenkins, R Moss and A Watson). The collaboration between scientists, conservationists and landowners that has marked the Langholm study proved invaluable and fruitful. We hope that it will continue into the future, enabling some of the issues that arise from the present study to be addressed and resolved.

Throughout the study, all raptors in the Langholm area were rigorously protected and allowed to breed freely, while other legally controllable predators (notably foxes and crows) were killed as before, and the heather was managed as usual. The estate gamekeepers thus played a significant role in the study. The main raptors of importance were the hen harrier and the peregrine.

As in any study of this type, the most rigorous approach scientifically would have been experimental, comparing the grouse numbers in the Langholm area where raptors were protected with grouse numbers in similar areas from which raptors were removed, reversing the treatments after a period of years. However, for various reasons, including the conservation status of raptors, this procedure was considered impractical and unacceptable, and instead a non-experimental approach was adopted, measuring everything necessary to assess the impact of raptors. We did, however, have the benefit of bag records from two other moors in the same region, where raptors were much scarcer than at Langholm, but where the annual bags had previously fluctuated in parallel with those at Langholm.

As you will read in this report, the numbers of harriers nesting at Langholm increased greatly during the study, and the numbers of peregrines rather less so. In the latter years of the study, predation by these birds appeared to have been sufficient to hold the grouse population at a continuing low level, preventing the population from cycling and giving post-breeding numbers too low to support driven grouse shooting. The situation at Langholm, where through sheep grazing the moor now consists of a mixture of heather and grassy areas, favoured high densities of harriers, giving a naturally high harrier/grouse ratio. This situation may not hold on more heather-dominated moors elsewhere, which are less favourable to harriers; but it is now typical of many heather/grass moors south of the Highlands that have been affected by sheep grazing in recent decades. We hope, therefore, that this publication will contribute significantly to the ongoing debate on grouse and raptors, and also to the wider issues of land use, economics and conservation in the British uplands.

It remains for us to express our gratitude to all the organisations and individuals who have contributed so much to the project over the years, and particularly to Steve Redpath (Institute of Terrestrial Ecology) and Simon Thirgood (Game Conservancy Trust), who did most of the hard work.

The Earl of Dalkeith
Professor Ian Newton

Summary

1. The objective of this study was to examine the impact of raptor predation on red grouse numbers. The study was based at Langholm in south-west Scotland, but was also extended, in part, to five other study moors elsewhere in Scotland. On these moors, raptors were protected but the numbers of foxes and crows were controlled by gamekeepers. Each year, during 1992–96, we estimated on each moor the abundance of grouse, songbirds (mainly meadow pipits) and small mammals (mainly field voles), and monitored the numbers, breeding success and diet of hen harriers and peregrines. At Langholm we also studied grouse mortality and raptor hunting behaviour, in addition to measuring a number of habitat features. Finally, we examined records of grouse bags to see how the number of grouse shot changed in the presence of breeding raptors.

2. By use of aerial photographs, we estimated that 48% of heather-dominant vegetation was lost from Langholm moor between 1948 and 1988, mostly at lower altitudes. This loss of heather and consequent increase in grass were attributed to heavy grazing by sheep. Grouse bags on the same moor have shown a consistent and significant downward trend since 1913, and have also shown six-year fluctuations with the last peak in 1990. Given that raptor breeding densities were thought to be very low before 1990, it is extremely unlikely that raptors were responsible for either the long-term decline or the fluctuations in grouse bags.

3. On four study moors, the average density of breeding harriers increased year on year for four years following protection from suspected illegal killing and other interference. During 1992–96, harrier numbers at Langholm increased from two to 14 breeding females. Peregrine numbers were generally more constant over time, although at Langholm numbers increased from three to five or six pairs. From October to March, the numbers of peregrines and harriers seen varied considerably between geographical areas. At Langholm, a similar number of peregrine sightings were recorded each winter, but sightings of female harriers fluctuated in line with grouse density.

4. In each year, raptor predation in spring removed on average 30% of the potential breeding stock of grouse, and in the summers of 1995 and 1996 harrier predation removed on average 37% of grouse chicks. Most of these adult and chick losses were probably additive to other forms of mortality, and together reduced the post-breeding numbers of grouse by an estimated 50% within a single breeding season. In each year, raptors also killed on average 30% of the grouse between October and March, but it was not possible to determine what proportion of these grouse would have survived in the absence of raptors. A simple, mathematical model of the grouse population at Langholm, combining the estimated reduction in breeding productivity with observed density dependence in winter loss, predicted that over two years, in the absence of breeding raptors, grouse breeding numbers would have increased by 1.3 times and post-breeding numbers would have increased by 2.5 times.

5. Over the course of the study, we found no evidence that predation on adult grouse at Langholm was directly influenced by any of the habitat features we measured. However, a greater proportion of harrier attacks on grouse broods occurred in areas with a mixture of heather and grass, as opposed to pure heather or pure grass stands, than expected from the proportion of grouse broods located by us in that habitat.

6. Throughout the study, grouse density on Langholm moors in July averaged 33 birds per 0.5 km² and numbers did not change significantly from year to year. Grouse bags did not peak in 1996 as expected from past records. In contrast, grouse

bags on two other nearby moors, which had previously fluctuated in synchrony with those at Langholm, increased to high levels in 1996. These moors held only low densities of raptors. Predation by much larger numbers of raptors at Langholm was considered the most likely explanation for the continued low grouse density and low grouse bags on this moor during the study period. Bags on other moors where raptors were protected did not exhibit the same patterns as observed at Langholm. This was either because raptor numbers remained at low density, or because driven shooting was already not viable by the time raptor protection occurred.

7. Where raptors were not persecuted, breeding densities of harriers and peregrines varied considerably between different moors and were not primarily related to grouse densities. The highest breeding densities of harriers occurred on moors where meadow pipits and small mammals were most abundant. These prey appeared to prefer moors with a high ratio of grass/heather. Peregrine breeding densities were lower in the Highlands than in the north of England, probably because of differences in the abundance of pigeons, their main prey. In the absence of persecution we thus predict that raptor numbers will be greatest on southern rather than northern moors and on moors with a high ratio of grass/heather. Extrapolating from data on harrier and peregrine diet, we judge that the impact of raptor predation within moors will be greatest when grouse densities go below approximately 12 pairs per km^2.

Chapter 1

Portraits of an immature female hen harrier (upper) and peregrine falcon

1. Introduction

BACKGROUND AND AIMS OF PROJECT

In the British uplands, large areas of heather moorland are managed for the production of red grouse[*]. This form of land use is of considerable economic importance, complementing for individual landowners the income available from other land uses, such as hill sheep farming and forestry. Grouse management maintains landscapes that are of global importance, not only for their unique character, but also for the wildlife they sustain. The principal goal of this management is to maximise the number of grouse available for shooting in the autumn. To this end gamekeepers are employed primarily to manage the habitat and to control the predators.

Since gamebird populations were first managed, predator control was assumed to be necessary in order to produce large numbers of grouse. Lord Lovat clearly indicated this in 1911, when he wrote in his report *The grouse in health and disease:* 'There is no room for vermin and an active keeper on the same beat'. He went on to list the main predators as fox, stoat, crow and peregrine. Interestingly, the hen harrier was not mentioned, presumably because it had already been effectively eradicated by keepers from mainland Britain by that time (Watson 1977). Substantial numbers of predators were killed each year on grouse moors, as studies of old game books reveal. For example, in the 1930s, gamekeepers on Langholm moor in the Scottish Borders killed an annual average of 169 foxes, 562 stoats and weasels, 206 crows and 107 'hawks' (see also Harvie-Brown 1906; Nethersole-Thompson 1951). Such levels of control soon greatly reduced the distribution and abundance of raptors in Britain (Newton 1979). In response to declines in numbers of birds of prey, full legal protection was introduced in 1954 for all raptors except sparrowhawks (protected in 1961), though illegal killing has continued in many areas. Recent evidence suggests that illegal control of certain species is still widespread (eg Etheridge, Summers & Green 1997), and sufficient to limit their distributions and numbers (Newton 1979).

[*] *Scientific names of all species are given in Appendix 1*

Gamekeepers continue to kill birds of prey because they see them as a threat to their grouse stocks and, by extension, to their jobs. However, conservation bodies have argued that these birds are important components of natural communities and of conservation concern because of their relatively low numbers. They have also pointed to the lack of convincing evidence about possible impacts of raptors on grouse stocks.

Articles in the popular press over the last few years have revealed that the role of raptors in limiting red grouse populations continues to be a source of controversy and conflict. Under these circumstances, there is an obvious need to understand the importance of predation by raptors in relation to other factors affecting grouse numbers.

The main objective of this study was to find whether raptor predation could limit red grouse numbers at levels substantially lower than would occur in the absence of raptors. The associated applied question was: is it possible to run an economically viable grouse moor and allow raptors to breed freely? In this introduction, we consider previous red grouse research and the main avian predators of red grouse, then examine some relevant theoretical aspects of predation and discuss the evidence for predators limiting prey numbers from other studies. Finally, we introduce the approach we have taken in this study.

RED GROUSE AND THEIR PREDATORS

Ecology of red grouse

Red grouse are monogamous, territorial birds which live in the heather-dominant moorlands of the British Isles. The principal food of the adult grouse is heather, although other plants such as cottongrass and bilberry are frequently consumed in spring and summer. The cocks establish their territories in the autumn, which they defend vigorously until the next summer, though they may temporarily abandon them during harsh weather in winter (Jenkins, Watson & Miller 1963).

Nests tend to be situated in mature heather and egg laying generally starts in late April. Soon after hatching, the brood is taken to areas rich in arthropods (insects and spiders). These invertebrates are an important source of protein for small chicks, and broods can travel up to 400 m each day to reach such areas (Hudson 1986a). The main period of chick mortality occurs in the first ten days after hatching, before chicks can fully control their own body temperature. Variation in grouse chick survival between years and between areas has been explained by the condition of the hen prior to laying (eg Moss *et al.* 1981), by the weather conditions after hatching (eg Erikstad 1985), and by the availability of arthropod prey for the young chicks (Hudson 1986a).

Grouse are usually still in family groups by 12 August, the start of the shooting season. Shooting levels are traditionally set according to estimates of July density, with driven grouse shooting occurring above densities of roughly 60 birds per square kilometre (Hudson 1992). Grouse can sometimes occur at remarkably high densities, with July numbers in excess of 600 birds per km^2 counted on moors in northern England (Hudson 1986a). By September or October, grouse family groups break up as territories become re-established.

Grouse suffer from a number of different parasites, of which two can have a major impact on population levels. The nematode *Trichostrongylus tenuis* is the main cause of grouse disease (see below), and the sheep tick is a vector for the louping ill virus. Both diseases can cause high levels of mortality in grouse.

Further details of red grouse ecology may be found in Watson and Jenkins (1964), Watson and Miller (1971), Cramp and Simmons (1980), Lawton (1990), Hudson (1992) and Hudson and Newborn (1995), in addition to the literature cited above.

Predators of red grouse
Foxes and crows are thought to be the most significant predators of red grouse and are vigorously controlled by gamekeepers. Surprisingly little work has been done to estimate their impact on grouse populations, although Hudson (1992) presented some correlative evidence which suggested that reductions in the level of control of foxes and crows led to a reduction in the numbers of grouse shot. These predators, along with mustelids (ie stoats and weasels), can be legally controlled through snaring, trapping or shooting, and records of numbers killed suggest that populations of crows and foxes in Scotland may have increased in recent decades (Hudson 1992).

Several raptor species prey upon red grouse, though to different extents. Grouse can form a major component of the diets of hen harriers, peregrines and golden eagles. They occur to a lesser degree in the diets of common buzzard and goshawk, and are taken rarely by short-eared owls, sparrowhawks, kestrels and merlins. Throughout this study, we have focused on the hen harrier and peregrine falcon, as these two species are of greatest concern to the grouse manager.

Harriers start their sky-dancing displays over prospective breeding sites in early spring and eggs are laid from mid-April onwards, in nests built on the ground in tall heather (Redpath *et al.* 1997). Harriers are not strongly territorial, although they will defend a small area around their nest site, and separate pairs can nest within 500 m of one another. Unlike most raptors, they can be polygynous, in that one male may mate with more than one female. Harrier chicks usually hatch in late May and start flying some six weeks later, around mid-July. Three weeks after fledging, the family groups leave their natal site and presumably split up. Harriers hunt low over vegetation and catch their prey on the ground. More details of harrier ecology may be found in Watson (1977) and Cramp and Simmons (1980).

In contrast to harriers, peregrines are highly territorial and pairs generally do not tolerate other peregrines breeding nearby. They usually nest on cliff ledges, though they will occasionally nest on sloping ground, and the nests of different pairs tend to be evenly spaced through suitable habitat. They start breeding earlier than harriers, and usually lay three or four eggs in early April. Chicks hatch about four weeks later in early May and fledge after a further six weeks.

Families stay together for at least two months after fledging, and then the young disperse. They usually catch their prey in the air, though the occurrence of mammals in the diet shows that they catch some food on the ground. More details of peregrine ecology may be found in Cramp and Simmons (1980) and Ratcliffe (1993).

Recent surveys have aimed to find the total breeding numbers of hen harriers and peregrines in Britain (Bibby & Etheridge 1993; Crick & Ratcliffe 1995). The total harrier breeding population was estimated at around 630 females in 1988–89, and the total peregrine breeding population at around 1280 pairs in 1991. Grouse moors provide an important habitat for both species, particularly the harrier, the majority of which nest on heather moorland. Peregrine numbers have now recovered from the impact of organochlorine pesticides in the 1950s and 1960s, to densities that are probably greater than they were before the second world war (when control was rife). In contrast, harrier numbers appear to be stable or declining, despite large areas of suitable but unoccupied habitat in certain parts of the range (Etheridge *et al.* 1997). Their numbers were dramatically reduced by persecution before the end of the last century, and it is only since the second world war that they have become re-established in mainland Britain, with the general decline in keepering levels over that period and with the help of afforestation programmes which have provided suitable unkeepered habitat in young plantations. Etheridge *et al.* (1997) estimated that both annual survival and breeding success of harriers were significantly lower on grouse moors than elsewhere, because of illegal control on grouse moors. Such persecution may account for the fact that the national population is not increasing.

SOME GENERAL POINTS ABOUT PREDATION

In this section we introduce the ideas and terminology which will be used throughout this publication, drawing from general texts (see Krebs 1985; Crawley 1992; Begon, Harper & Townsend 1996) and from more specific reviews by Sinclair (1989), Newton (1993), Murdoch (1994) and Turchin (1995).

Where possible, we illustrate the issues with examples from previous studies on grouse.

Density dependence and population regulation

The population size of any species is determined by the balance between gains from breeding and immigration, and losses from mortality and emigration. If the rate of either gains or losses is unrelated to the density of the bird at the time, it is said to be *density independent*. If the rate of gain decreases or the rate of loss increases with density, it is said to be *density dependent*. Conversely, if the rate of loss decreases with an increase in density, it is said to be *inversely density dependent*. Consider the simple situation in Figure 1.1. Here a population is subject to density-independent gains and density-dependent losses. In other words, as density increases, per capita breeding success and immigration remain constant, but per capita losses through mortality and emigration increase. The point where gains equal losses can be thought of as an equilibrium density. The process which sets the location of this equilibrium is termed *limitation* and the factors which cause changes in gains and losses are *limiting factors*. This is true whether or not they act in a manner which correlates with density.

Any factor which influences losses or gains is a limiting factor and so, by definition, is

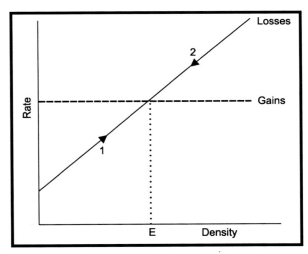

Figure 1.1 Diagrammatic representation of how rates of change vary in relation to density for a hypothetical population. This population is subject to density-dependent losses and density-independent gains. The point where the lines cross is the equilibrium density (E). In part 1 of the Figure gains exceed losses so the population increases at these densities. In part 2, losses exceed gains so the population declines

involved in limiting a population. In part 1 of the graph, losses are less than gains and so the population increases. In part 2, losses exceed gains and so the population declines. Therefore, if for some reason the population is pushed from this equilibrium, by a hard winter for example, the density-dependent response will in time return the population to its equilibrium. If the density dependence is strong (a steep line in this graph), a small drop in density will lead to a large drop in the rate of loss, allowing the population to increase rapidly. Weak density dependence (a shallow line) will mean only a slight drop in the rate of loss and hence a slow rate of recovery. This process of return to equilibrium is termed *regulation* and the factors causing this are *regulatory factors.* Any regulatory factor must clearly act in a density-dependent manner.

In reality, a variety of processes, both density-dependent and density-independent, will act on a population at any one time. The relative importance of these processes, and therefore the position of the equilibrium, is also likely to vary. As an example, any grouse population is likely to be limited by factors such as weather, heather quality, predation, parasites and competition for territories. If, over time, the quality of the habitat were to decline, the equilibrium density, ie the density at which losses equal gains, would decline. In other words, regardless of other factors, the moor would support fewer grouse. The relative importance of these processes, and hence the equilibrium densities, are likely to vary between moors. In effect, the aim of grouse management is to try to maximise the equilibrium density, by reducing losses through predation and parasitism and increasing gains through breeding success.

Population cycles

Regulatory processes often do not respond immediately to changes in prey density. If, for example, a grouse population is regulated by parasites, it may take up to a year for parasite numbers to change in response to a change in grouse density. Here the impact of parasites will still show density dependence, but the effects will be delayed. This process of *delayed density dependence* can cause a population to

exhibit regular fluctuations or cycles. Consider a population increasing from low density with parasites acting with a time lag of one year. When the grouse population increases, parasite numbers also increase but are one year behind, and this means that grouse numbers continue to rise. In other words, the grouse population overshoots the equilibrium before it is driven down by increasing numbers of parasites. As the grouse numbers decline, so do the parasites, and the cycle begins again.

Cycles are common attributes of grouse populations. They have been studied extensively, and for red grouse two main explanations have been proposed. Hudson showed that cycles on English moors with high rainfall could be caused by the impact of the parasite *Trichostrongylus tenuis* on grouse breeding success (eg Hudson, Dobson & Newborn 1985; Hudson & Dobson 1990; Hudson 1992), whereas Moss and colleagues showed that changes in the social structure and associated territorial behaviour within the grouse population could cause cycles on drier Scottish moors (eg Moss & Watson 1985; Mountford *et al.* 1990; Moss, Watson & Parr 1996). Whatever the causes, it is clear that cycles of red grouse numbers occur in areas where predator numbers are controlled. Grouse numbers can decline and can remain at low densities for a number of years in the virtual absence of predators. To assess the impact of predation on a cyclic population, it is therefore necessary to study that population for at least the length of the cycle, because any depression in numbers may be caused by factors other than predation.

Compensatory and additive mortality

If Figure 1.1 represents a grouse population on an area without raptors, what would happen if raptors were introduced? We might predict that raptors would increase the annual mortality rate of the grouse, so leading to a reduced equilibrium density. However, this would not necessarily happen: an increase in predation might be offset by the improved survival of the remaining individuals, so that there would be no increase in the annual mortality rate. This improved survival could *compensate* for the increased predation by raptors. If the grouse killed by raptors were lost from the population over and above the numbers that would otherwise have died, then predation would be *additive* and the population would be reduced as a result. Similarly, removing one predator species may not necessarily lead to more grouse as there may be a *compensatory* increase in the numbers lost to another predator species. Additive and compensated mortality lie at opposite ends of a continuum, as intermediate situations occur in which predation can be partly additive and partly compensated. The important point is that predation does not necessarily have the impact on population levels that would be expected simply from the number of individuals killed.

Compensation can come about in a number of different ways. Consider our theoretical grouse population to which we have introduced raptor predation. Let us assume, for the sake of argument, that this population is regulated by density-dependent winter mortality, so that the rate of winter losses increases with grouse density. One factor which is clearly important in influencing the effect of the raptor predation is that of timing. If the raptors kill grouse before the winter, their effects on spring density could be compensated, because they will reduce the density and therefore the level of winter loss. However, if they kill after the density-dependent losses have occurred, then their effects on spring density will be additive. Whether the density-dependent process is predation by other predators, starvation, dispersal, competition for territories, or parasitism, compensation can still occur.

The strength of the density dependence will also be important in determining the extent to which additional raptor predation affects the grouse population. If raptors kill grouse before the winter and the density dependence is strong (a steep line), then all the raptor predation could be compensated through a marked reduction in winter losses. However, weak density dependence will mean that the rate of winter loss will not change greatly, so the population may not compensate for the entire loss.

A further consideration is the density of the grouse population relative to its equilibrium. If the grouse population is above its equilibrium,

then there may be surplus grouse present. Consider a grouse population in which territories are the main limiting factor and where a lack of a territory means that the birds cannot breed. If there are more birds than territories, raptor predation is less likely to lead to a loss of breeding grouse, either because birds removed were non-territorial and would have died anyway without breeding, or because they were territorial birds which were replaced from the non-territorial surplus.

There are two clear examples of compensatory mortality occurring in grouse populations. First, Jenkins *et al.* (1963) and later Watson (1985) showed that in a high density grouse population non-territorial 'surplus' or 'doomed' grouse were the ones most likely to be killed by predators in the winter, and that whenever a territorial bird was killed its place was rapidly taken by a previously non-territorial one. Consequently, predation had little or no effect on grouse breeding numbers in the spring. Second, Parker (1984) examined predation of ptarmigan by crows and found that, when he killed crows, there was no subsequent increase in ptarmigan post-breeding numbers, because of a compensatory increase in mustelid predation.

Numerical, functional and total response
There are two central components to predation (Solomon 1949). The total number of prey killed on any area is a product of the number of predators present and the number of prey killed per predator. The way in which the number of predators on an area changes with prey density is termed the *numerical response*, and the way the number of prey killed per predator changes with prey density is termed the *functional response* (Holling 1959). The net result of these two responses has been termed the *total response*. Although developed for simple systems with a predator and one prey type, these relationships provide a useful conceptual framework when considering interactions within more complex predator/prey systems, like the one discussed here.

The way in which raptors respond to changes in prey density is important in determining their effects on prey. In this study we needed to find how raptor numbers and diet varied in relation to changes in grouse density. Raptors may respond numerically to their prey in three main ways:

- by settling and breeding at higher density (eg Hagen 1969; Hamerstrom 1986; Korpimaki & Norrdahl 1991),
- by raising more young per pair when prey are abundant (eg Hagen 1969; Newton 1979), and
- by spending more time hunting in areas of high prey density (eg Kenward, Marcström & Karlbom 1981; Keith & Rusch 1988).

Three main types of functional response are illustrated in Figure 1.2. These graphs assume that there is no numerical response to the prey and illustrate how a change in the shape of the functional response can influence the percentage of prey eaten. If predators responded numerically as well, this would have the effect on the total response of reducing the percentage eaten at low density and increasing the percentage eaten at high density. If we can determine how many grouse individual raptors kill, how many raptors there are, and how these two measures vary with grouse density, we will be in a better position to assess how the overall number of grouse removed by raptors (ie the total response) varies according to grouse densities.

Generalist and specialist predators

Raptors which live on grouse moors tend to be *generalist predators*, feeding on a variety of prey species. For example, Ratcliffe (1993) lists up to 50 different prey species taken by peregrine falcons in various British upland localities, and Watson (1977) lists 32 species taken by hen harriers from sites in south-west Scotland. Although both species take a wide variety of prey, one or two prey species tend to predominate in the diet in any given area, such as meadow pipits for harriers and feral pigeons for peregrines. The varied diets of these predators mean that they may show weaker numerical responses to one particular prey species compared to *specialist predators*. The short-eared owl is probably the predator closest to a specialist in upland Britain, because it

feeds almost exclusively on small mammals, especially the short-tailed field vole. Owl numbers can fluctuate dramatically from one year to the next in relation to the abundance of voles. Interestingly, a similar situation occurs with the hen harrier in other parts of the world, where its numbers fluctuate markedly from year to year in line with its main rodent prey (see Hamerstrom (1986) in North America; Hagen (1969) and Korpimaki (1985) in Scandinavia).

Generalist predators can theoretically have a considerable impact on their prey. If their main prey species declines for whatever reason, these predators might switch to eating other species. This hypothesis has been proposed as the cause of cycles in grouse numbers in Scandinavia and North America (Keith *et al.* 1977; Angelstam, Lindström & Widén 1984; Lindström *et al.* 1994). In these regions, mammals (voles in

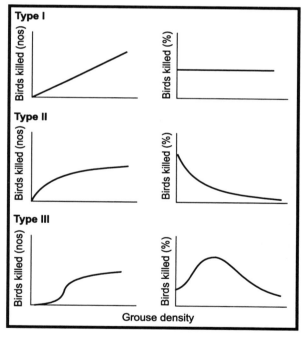

Figure 1.2 Three hypothetical functional response curves (types I, II and III) for a predator killing grouse. The graphs on the left indicate three relationships between grouse density and the number of grouse killed, whilst the graphs on the right indicate how the numbers killed translate into a percentage of the population killed. Type I relationships show a linear relationship between grouse density and number killed, which produces a constant % kill, or density independence. Type II relationships show an asymptotic curve, with a steep increase in the number of grouse killed initially, followed by a levelling off; this produces a declining % kill, suggesting that predation is most important at low density (inverse density dependence). Type III relationships show a sigmoidal functional response; this produces density dependence at low grouse densities, but inverse density dependence at high density (source Crawley 1992, Figure 3.2, p52)

Scandinavia and hares in Canada) were the main prey and, when mammal numbers crashed, various predators switched to gamebirds, so driving their numbers down. Eventually the predators themselves declined, thus enabling the prey to increase again. It has also been proposed that generalist predators may prevent populations of their main prey from cycling, as predator numbers are maintained at sufficiently high levels by a variety of prey types to stop the main prey from increasing above a certain threshold (eg Hanski, Hansson & Henttonen 1991).

In any study of predation, therefore, it is important that the predator and the main prey are not considered in isolation, but examined in the context of alternative prey species.

CAN PREDATORS LIMIT THEIR PREY?

Field experiments
In a recent paper, Newton (1993) reviewed 31 field experiments that have been conducted to find the impact of predators on their avian prey, although only one included the removal of raptors. Predator removal experiments represent the clearest way of finding whether or not predators can substantially reduce the numbers of their prey. These predator removal experiments were performed mainly on gamebirds and ducks, but they did not all measure the same parameters and were of variable quality. In summary,
- 86% (of 28) showed an increase in prey nest success following predator removal,
- 69% (of 16) showed an increase in post-breeding numbers,
- 62% (of 16) showed an increase in subsequent breeding numbers.

Predation was therefore shown to be important in most field experiments, but increases in breeding success following predator removal did not necessarily lead to increases in subsequent breeding density. The increases in breeding density which were observed under predator removal varied up to two-fold.

Most of these experiments were conducted on ground-nesting prey species and on generalist predators, a combination in which predation might be expected to be important. Although most of the experiments did not include the removal of raptors, there is no inherent reason why the removal of generalist raptors would give different results from generalist mammalian predators. Newton emphasised two other relevant points:
- experiments where only one predator was removed showed no subsequent increases in the prey, probably because of compensatory predation by other predators;
- in some experiments predation was greatly influenced by the availability of alternative prey (usually voles or rabbits) and by habitat features such as nesting cover.

Observational studies of predation on red grouse
There have been two main earlier studies of predation on red grouse in Scotland. Both studies were on keepered grouse moors, where both mammalian and avian predators were controlled.

Jenkins and colleagues investigated patterns of grouse mortality in Glen Esk over five years, and found that grouse mortality rates were high (Jenkins, Watson & Miller 1963, 1967). They estimated from tagged grouse that only one third of grouse present in autumn survived to the next autumn. Thus, even in these areas where predators were controlled, around two-thirds of the grouse were lost to predators, hunters and other mortality agents between one year and the next.

Jenkins, Watson and Miller (1964) also found that maximum predation coincided with the periods of grouse dispersal in early and late winter, and showed that the predators concentrated on the non-territorial birds as opposed to the territory owners. They concluded that predation was unimportant in limiting either the numbers of breeding grouse or the numbers available for shooting. The idea that predators were not killing territory owners was investigated further by Watson (1985), who compared winter mortality rates in tagged territory owners against tagged non-territorial birds. He showed clear differences, with virtually all the territorial grouse surviving, whilst most of the non-territorial grouse were killed or otherwise disappeared before spring.

In contrast, Hudson more recently found that the overwinter survival rates of territorial and non-territorial grouse in upper Speyside were similar (Hudson 1990, 1992). He went on to suggest that at least part of the winter predation was additive, and reduced the density of breeding birds in spring. Two key differences may help explain the divergent conclusions of these studies. First, the number of predators in the Scottish Highlands appears to have increased from the 1950s (Watson & Moss 1990; Hudson 1992). As Watson and Moss (1990) point out: 'it is possible that larger numbers of predators are now limiting spring numbers of red grouse and are also reducing summering adult stocks and breeding success'. The second difference between the two studies was that they were conducted on moors with very different grouse densities. The earlier study was conducted on an area where spring grouse densities were on average 66 individuals per km², whilst in Speyside average spring densities were only 20 individuals per km². Lower densities may mean that fewer non-territorial grouse are present, so that predation falls more heavily on the territorial birds and is thus more likely to be additive (Hudson 1992).

The role of predation in limiting grouse numbers needs to be considered separately for breeding numbers in spring and post-breeding numbers available for harvesting in autumn. For the grouse manager, the latter is the critical measure, though this measure is itself a product of spring density and breeding success.

The principal avian predator of grouse chicks is the hen harrier and two studies have examined the impact of this predator on red grouse breeding success. Picozzi (1978) estimated that harriers removed 7.4% of the grouse from a moor with a high density of grouse (>40 female grouse per km²), whilst Redpath (1991) suggested that grouse at lower densities (<10 female grouse per km²) were likely to experience higher levels of predation. He went on to show that harriers could account for most of the grouse chick mortality after the first two weeks of age. On average, moors with harriers produced 17% fewer grouse chicks than moors where no harriers bred, although it was unclear whether this reduced the bag and subsequent spring densities of grouse. This work highlighted the need to find what influences harrier numbers, as this is a principal factor contributing to overall grouse chick losses.

HABITAT QUALITY

The ability of a predator to catch prey may, to a certain extent, depend on the habitat in which the prey live. Habitat quality is a notoriously vague term, but for our purposes we consider it to have two components: food and structure. Good-quality moorland for grouse can be considered to consist of heather rich in nitrogen and phosphorus, bog flushes rich in arthropods, and vegetation of sufficient height and density to provide cover from adverse weather and predators. A number of studies of red grouse have suggested that food quality is important in sustaining high densities of grouse (Jenkins et al. 1963; Picozzi 1968; Moss 1969; Miller, Watson & Jenkins 1970). In addition, Watson et al. (1984) suggested that adults feeding on high-quality food could be more vigilant, and could thus better defend themselves against predators.

The structure of the habitat is also important, especially for ground-nesting species during the breeding season. This particular aspect has not been studied in red grouse, although for partridge Rands (1988) found that nests were more successful when placed in good cover than in poor cover. Watson and Miller (1976) indicated that grouse rarely foraged further than 14 m from mature heather, presumably to lessen the risks of predation. In support of this view, Redpath (1992) twice observed grouse broods as they were approached by a hunting harrier. Both interactions occurred on the edge between young and mature heather, and both times the female took her young to the cover of the mature heather before the harrier arrived.

The relationship between habitat quality and predation in red grouse has yet to be accurately quantified, although any study of predation must take into account the quality of the habitat. It is possible, for example, that grouse might be more vulnerable to predators on a 'low-quality' grouse moor, than on a 'high-quality' one.

APPROACH

To the layman, the study of predation may seem relatively straightforward, as any predator that removes prey will be expected to reduce the numbers of its prey, and thus future numbers of grouse. Several species of raptors have been recorded killing red grouse, but it would be wrong to infer that they must necessarily have a significant impact on grouse populations. As we have seen, a number of factors have to be taken into account, such as the relative densities of raptors and grouse, the availability of alternative prey, the timing and selectivity of predation, and whether the predation is additive or compensatory. Indeed, if predators removed heavily parasitised individuals (as shown by Hudson, Dobson and Newborn 1992a), they may actually benefit the grouse population.

The clearest way of assessing the impact of predation is through controlled experiments, in which predators are removed from an area and prey numbers monitored for comparison with numbers in a control area where the predators are left. Good examples of this type of work have been conducted on predators of gamebirds in Sweden (Marcström, Engren & Kenward 1988) and in England (Tapper, Potts & Brockless 1996). However, for birds of prey, removal experiments were considered unacceptable, so the alternative was to observe patterns of mortality and population trends in areas where grouse were subject to different natural levels of raptor predation.

The first step in this study was to determine the level of raptor predation in relation to the density of red grouse by monitoring both the grouse and the raptors. Studies of grouse, through counts, carcase searches and radio-tracking, allowed us to determine the proportion of grouse killed by raptors. Studies of predators allowed us to estimate the number of grouse killed per predator and the number of predators present. Both predator diet and number are likely to vary as a function of prey density, so it was necessary to study these aspects over a

wide range of prey densities. In addition to assessing predation levels, we determined the parasite burdens of the killed birds, the age and sex class to which they belonged, and the timing of predation. With this information, we could begin to assess the extent to which predation could limit grouse numbers. We were helped in this assessment by comparative information from other study moors, some of which had fewer raptors than Langholm moor.

As we have focused both on the raptors and on the grouse, the publication is divided accordingly. In Chapter 2, we introduce the study areas and historical information on heather cover and grouse bags, and Chapters 3–10 are arranged around the following basic questions.

- How do harrier and peregrine breeding numbers vary over time and between study moors? (Chapter 3)
- What factors influence the distribution of hunting harriers and peregrines? (Chapter 4)
- How does harrier and peregrine diet vary in relation to numbers of grouse? (Chapter 5)
- How many grouse do harriers and peregrines remove from a population over the breeding season? (Chapter 6)
- What is the pattern of grouse mortality within a population? (Chapter 7)
- What impact do raptors have on a grouse population? (Chapter 8)
- Is there an interaction between habitat and predation? (Chapter 9)
- How have the long-term patterns of grouse bags changed with the presence of breeding raptors? (Chapter 10)

In Chapter 11 the findings are brought together in a general discussion.

GLOSSARY

Alternative prey – used here to describe prey other than red grouse on which harriers and peregrines feed.

Additive mortality – mortality which leads to an increase in the overall mortality rate within a population.

Beat – an area of a grouse moor managed by a specific keeper and consisting of a number of drives.

Bigamy – referred to here as a mating system where a male mates with two females at one time.

Compensation – mechanism whereby the effects of mortality do not lead to an increase in the overall mortality rate within a population.

Delayed density dependence – a process, such as mortality, whose effects show a lagged increase with the density of a population.

Density – numbers of individuals in a given area, usually 1 km² unless stated otherwise.

Density dependence – a process, such as mortality, whose effects increase with the density of a population.

Density independence – a process, such as mortality, whose effects do not vary in relation to the density of a population.

Dispersal – movement of organisms away from the place of birth (natal dispersal) or from any other specified area.

Dispersion – pattern of spacing of individuals in a population.

Drive – an area of grouse moor from which birds are driven by beaters over a line of grouse butts.

Equilibrium density – population density at which the rate of gains from births and immigration equals the rate of losses from deaths and emigration.

Fledgling – chick which has left the nest and is capable of flying.

Functional response – change in the rate of prey consumption by an individual predator in relation to the density of the prey.

Generalist predators – predators which feed on a wide variety of prey species.

Inverse density dependence – a process, such as mortality, whose effects decrease with the density of a population.

Lagomorph – a species such as rabbit and hare belonging to the family Leporidae.

Mustelid – species such as a stoat or weasel belonging to the family Mustelidae.

Nestling period – period which describes the time from hatching to fledging.

Nidifugous – chicks, such as grouse, which leave the nest soon after hatching.

Numerical response – change in the numbers of predators in relation to the density of the prey.

Passerine – a species which belongs to the order Passeriformes, commonly referred to as songbirds.

Persecution – term used to imply illegal killing and disturbance of protected raptor species.

Polygamy – a mating system in which the male pairs with more than one female at one time (polygyny) or a female pairs with more than one male (polyandry).

Population cycles – the rise and fall of annual population numbers with regular periodicity.

Population regulation – the process by which a population tends towards its equilibrium density when perturbed.

Population limitation – the process which sets the location of the equilibrium density in a population.

Post-fledging period – period which describes the time between fledging and dispersal of chicks.

Radio-tracking – study of individual grouse, marked with radio-transmitters which emit a pulse at a frequency specific to individual birds. The pulse is picked up by a receiver, revealing the presence of the bird.

Raptor – term used in the same sense as bird of prey.

Specialist predators – predators which specialise on one particular prey species.

Study moor – moorland estate where raptor numbers, diet and prey densities were measured.

Study site – areas within the study moor, used to count grouse and other prey species.

Surplus – term used to describe non-territorial grouse on a moor where all territories are occupied.

Total response – combined effect of predator functional and numerical responses on their prey.

Chapter 2

S M Redpath using radio-telemetry equipment, and female red grouse, with radio-collar, on her nest

2. Study areas and methods

- The study was conducted on six estates in Scotland. Two of them had driven grouse shooting when the project started in 1992. Intensive studies were conducted on Langholm moor.
- At Langholm, 48% of heather-dominant vegetation was estimated to have been lost between 1948 and 1988, mostly at lower altitudes.
- On all study moors we monitored raptor breeding numbers, breeding success and diet, in addition to counting grouse, passerines and small mammals. At Langholm we also studied grouse mortality and raptor hunting behaviour.
- We were able to distinguish between grouse killed by mammals and raptors, though away from nests and roost sites we were unable to distinguish between those killed by harriers and those killed by peregrines.
- Comparisons of the results from various techniques used to estimate raptor diet indicated that nest watches, pellets and prey remains gave similar measures of the importance of grouse in the diet.

INTRODUCTION

The study was based at Langholm in the Scottish Borders, on land owned by the Buccleuch Estates. At the start of the project in 1992, the Royal Society for the Protection of Birds (RSPB) and Raptor Study Group fieldworkers were asked to identify other grouse moors where harriers attempted to breed and where they believed there was no illegal raptor killing or disturbance. In addition to Langholm, nine other estates were identified in upland Britain. However, because of changes in management since the start of the project, four of these areas had to be dropped, leaving six moors for study in various parts of Scotland (Figure 2.1).

Figure 2.1 Map of Scotland showing the location of Langholm and the other study moors (A–E)

The intensity of work varied between the study moors. Detailed population studies on grouse were conducted only at Langholm. Harriers and peregrines on the other study moors were monitored to help us understand the numerical and functional responses of these raptors. This work involved counts of grouse, passerines and small mammals, along with studies of the number, diet and breeding success of raptors. In this Chapter we consider some of the historical background to the study areas and outline the methods we used.

HISTORICAL INFORMATION

Grouse bags

The number of grouse shot has frequently been used as an index of grouse densities, and bag records from specific areas provide an invaluable source of long-term information (Tapper 1992). Before examining trends in bag sizes within our study moors, however, we checked the relationship between bags and pre-shoot density at Langholm. This moor is divided into six areas or beats (see below), where the keeper has counted grouse each July since 1975. Four of these beats cover the main part of the moor and have been counted in every year. The keepers' counts were conducted on a varying number of drives in each beat, so an average count for each beat was taken. All counts conducted by the keepers were estimated to be in the region of 100 ha. There was a good relationship between the counts and the log-

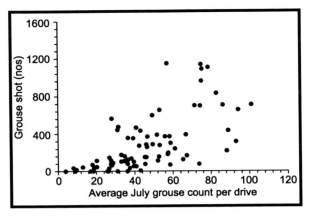

Figure 2.2 Relationship between the number of grouse shot and the number of grouse previously counted per drive in July within four beats at Langholm. Data were based on counts in 1975–96 and each point represents one beat in one year

transformed bags (controlling for beat: coefficient=0.024, $F_{1,76}$=48.04, P<0.001), suggesting that the bags were a good relative measure of July density at Langholm (Figure 2.2). The total bag was a product of the number of drives, set by the headkeeper (Figure 2.3i controlling for beat: log-transformed drives coefficient=0.012,

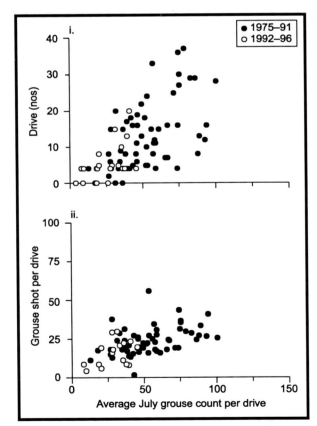

Figure 2.3 Relationships between (i) the number of drives shot in each year and the average number of grouse counted per drive in July within four beats at Langholm, and (ii) the number of grouse shot per drive and the average number of grouse counted per drive in July within four beats at Langholm. Data were based on counts in 1975–96 and each point represents one beat in one year

$F_{1,76}$=51.32, P<0.001) and the mean number of grouse shot per individual drive (Figure 2.3ii controlling for beat: coefficient=0.24, $F_{1,68}$=28.38, P<0.001).

Grouse bags for all six study moors were examined to assess the status of the grouse population at the start of the project relative to the previous 35 years (Figures 2.4 & 2.5). Only at Langholm and at moor C, in north-east Scotland, did driven grouse shooting consistently occur in the ten years before the project started, with average annual bags of over 36 birds per 100 ha. The Langholm grouse bags will be discussed in more detail in Chapter 10. On the remaining moors (A, B, D and E), grouse bags had declined greatly over the years preceding the project, and driven grouse shooting had stopped. These declines occurred in the 1960s and 1970s and were in line with national declines in grouse bags during this period (Hudson 1992). Although we have no information on raptor numbers at that time, the declines on the study moors were likely to be due to other factors. Hudson (1992) suggested that a combination of adverse weather and fox predation could account for the decline in grouse populations during the 1970s.

All six estates continue to employ gamekeepers who manage the habitat and control predators. Records of predators killed at Langholm show that the keepers killed at least as many foxes, stoats and

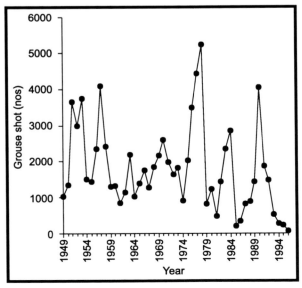

Figure 2.4 The total number of grouse shot in each year on Langholm moor in 1949–96

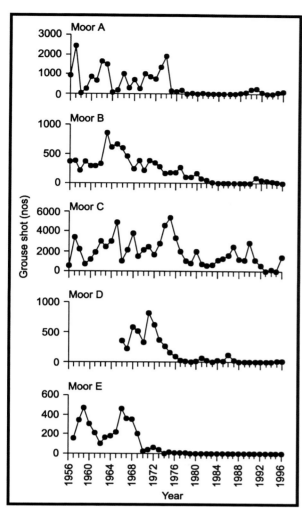

Figure 2.5 The total number of grouse shot in each year on five study moors around Scotland in 1956–96

was categorised in each hectare to the nearest 10%. We have included the heather areas on two neighbouring farms to the north of Langholm moor, as these were close to some harrier nests and therefore likely to have been hunted over by harriers. Heather ground to the west of the estate was not included as this was over 6 km from the nearest harrier nest and unlikely to have been regularly hunted by the study birds. The spatial distribution of heather cover was plotted for the two time periods (Figure 2.7). It was apparent that both the extent and density of heather had been greatly reduced between 1948 and 1988. In fact, we estimated from the data that the number of 1 ha squares with heather-dominant vegetation (ie >50% cover) had declined by 48% over the 40-year period. In addition, the extent of heather loss decreased with increasing altitude (Figure 2.8). The decline in heather cover was consistent with the effects of heavy grazing, with the heather being replaced largely by grass-dominant swards, particularly at lower elevations.

Because red grouse are dependent on heather, reductions in the amount of heather mean a loss in potential habitat.

crows per year during the project as they had in the preceding 12 years (Figure 2.6).

Habitat changes

Over the last 50 years the national decline in the area of heather moorland has been rapid and widespread (for details, see Thompson *et al.* 1995). One of the main factors considered responsible for this loss is overgrazing by sheep, whose densities have increased greatly in the British uplands over the last century (Sydes & Miller 1988). Aerial photographs, at the scale of 1:25 000, were taken of much of Britain in the 1940s and again in the 1980s. These provided us with an opportunity to assess the extent of habitat changes at Langholm in this period (1948–88).

Heather cover was assessed from the photographs using a stereoscope. Transparent sheets with a 1 ha grid were laid over the photographs and heather cover

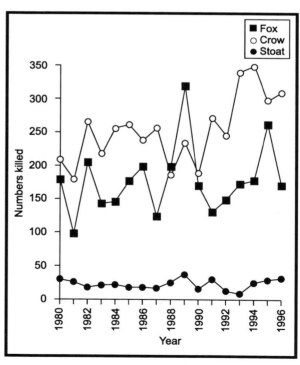

Figure 2.6 The numbers of foxes, crows and stoats killed in each year by keepers on Langholm estate from 1980 to 1996. The figures derive from a wider area than the grouse moor itself, but include the moor

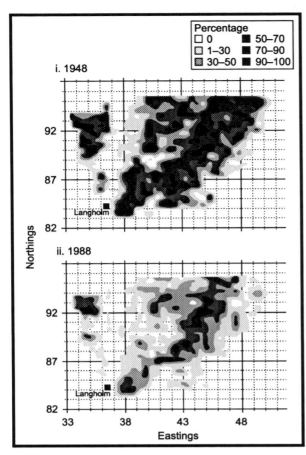

Figure 2.7 Changes in heather cover at Langholm from (i) 1948 to (ii) 1988, as assessed from aerial photographs. Heather cover was estimated for 25 ha blocks and divided into five bands from 1–30% to 90–100%. Plots are drawn using a Minitab contour plot facility. The dotted lines indicate a 100 ha grid

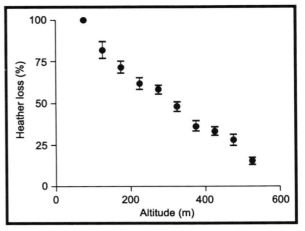

Figure 2.8 Relationship between altitude and estimates of the proportion of heather lost (mean) between 1948 and 1988 on 25 ha areas on Langholm moor

Using the 1988 aerial photographs, we also assessed heather cover within all the study moors (Table 2.1), by estimating heather cover in 10% of the 1 ha squares on each moor. These squares were chosen using a stratified random sampling technique and heather cover in each was estimated to the nearest 10%. From these samples an average cover was obtained and multiplied by the total area to give an estimate of overall heather cover.

Raptor availability
In addition to prey abundance and habitat availability, two other factors were considered of potential importance in determining the number of raptors available to breed on our study moors:

• the year that raptor protection was thought to have started on the estates covered, and
• the number of harrier chicks fledged in previous years within a 50 km radius of the estates concerned (Table 2.1).

This vegetation change may therefore partly explain the long-term decline in the number of grouse shot on this estate over the 40-year period (Chapter 10). To combat these changes, sheep densities on part of the estate were reduced in 1990, to enable heather to recover and thereby improve the moor for grouse.

Table 2.1 Summary of background information from the study moors. Areas of grouse moors were estimated by estate managers. Areas of heather were estimated from aerial photographs taken in 1988. The grouse bags indicate the average number of birds shot each year in the ten years preceding the study (1982–91). The minimum number of harriers fledged and percentage of nests which failed are based on RSPB data from 1988 to 1991 for harrier nests located within a 50 km radius of each moor. The location of the moors is shown in Figure 2.1

| | The study moors | | | | Within 50 km radius | |
Moor	Area grouse moor (ha)	Area heather 1988 (ha)	Average grouse bag (nos per 100 ha of grouse moor)	Year from which raptors were left unmolested	Minimum number of harriers fledged	% of known nests which failed
Langholm	4858	4701	1627 (33.5)	1990	7	67
A	2975	2603	63.1 (2.1)	1990	94	65
B	2095	1320	15.6 (0.7)	<1989	225	55
C	5281	3474	1370 (25.9)	1989	141	55
D	1500	1366	23.1 (1.5)	1987	110	54
E	4008	1906	0.2 (0.005)	1981	232	19

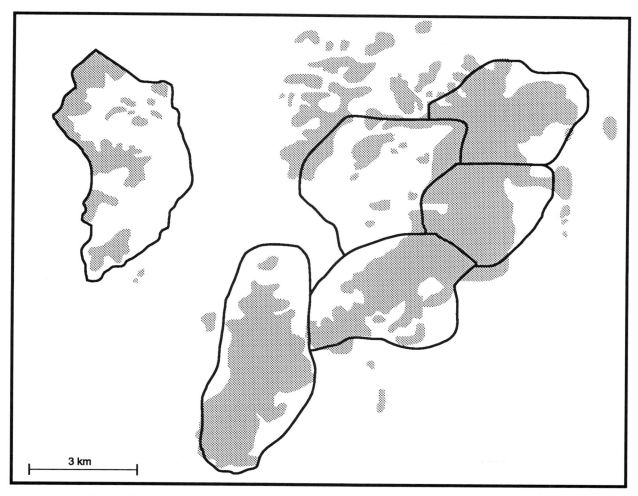

Figure 2.9 Distribution of >30% heather vegetation (shaded) and six grouse beats (solid lines) at Langholm. Heather distribution was estimated from 1988 aerial photographs and from ground-truthing on to 1:24 000 OS maps. Heather outside the beats to the north lies on neighbouring farms

This latter measure was derived from data collected by the RSPB over four years prior to this study (1988–91), when extensive searches for harrier nests were conducted. Both of these measures could have influenced the potential for increase in local raptor populations, especially harriers which are likely to have been persecuted more heavily than other species (see Chapter 3).

CURRENT HABITAT

In order to assess the amount of heather habitat at Langholm during the study, the 1988 photographs were validated by walking transects through the moor and assessing dominant ground cover over 1 ha areas around points which could be easily recognised from maps. Additionally, sketches were made of the surrounding land cover on Ordnance Survey (OS) (1:25 000) maps to allow more extensive, but less accurate, validations. For this vegetation map, heather moorland was taken as areas where *Calluna* formed more than 30% cover

of the 1 ha squares (Figure 2.9). A grid was drawn on a transparent sheet and placed on the map to enable the amount of heather and other habitat categories to be estimated in each hectare. A point was located at the centre of each square and the vegetation type underlying each point was assumed to be representative of the whole hectare. Using this technique, we estimated that, within the Langholm study area in 1994, heather moorland covered a total of 4145 ha (41.5 km²), with grass forming 11 593 ha and bracken 1282 ha. This estimate of heather cover compared with 4701 ha in 1988, though the two measures were not directly comparable because they were derived by different observers using slightly different techniques.

PREY COUNTS

Grouse counts

Twelve areas, each of 0.5 km², were demarcated and used for grouse counts at

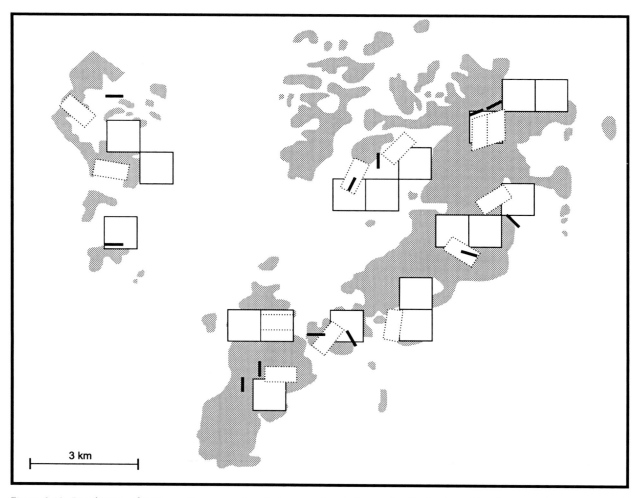

Figure 2.10 Distribution of prey count areas on Langholm moor in relation to the distribution of heather. Map shows 12 0.5 km² grouse count areas (dotted lines), 18 1 km² passerine count areas (solid lines) and 12 small mammal trap line locations (thick black lines)

Langholm, with two in each of the six traditional grouse beats (Figure 2.10). These areas were initially selected because they were representative of the vegetation within that beat and provided reasonable terrain for counting grouse. The count areas were widely spaced over the moorland in order to minimise the likelihood of counting the same individual grouse on different study sites. The statistical problems associated with 'pseudoreplication' are considered in Chapter 7.

On each of the other study moors, two areas of 1 km² were demarcated. Grouse densities were estimated on each area during the first two weeks in October, the first two weeks in April, and the last two weeks in July from counts with pointing dogs using standard techniques (Jenkins *et al.* 1963). Briefly, three parallel transects (six transects in the case of 1 km²) were walked through each area at 170 m intervals and the dog was

allowed to quarter the area up to approximately 85 m either side of the transect, pointing all the grouse encountered (Hudson & Newborn 1995). Grouse were classified as male, female or of unknown sex, and during the July counts adults were distinguished from juveniles. The same combination of pointing dog and observer was used throughout the five-year study. We also obtained estimates of grouse brood size and grouse chick abundance during the first week in June in each of the areas where raptor foraging was observed in summer, by working a pointing dog along a 2 km transect. Upon encountering a grouse brood, the dog was worked for a period of five minutes and all grouse chicks were captured, counted, weighed and measured, using wing length as an index of age.

Passerine counts
Passerines (songbirds) were counted using line transects (Bibby, Burgess & Hill 1992).

Three 1 km² squares were selected at random from each of the six traditional grouse beats at Langholm, giving a total of 18 squares (Figure 2.10). Six 1 km² squares were selected at random from each of the other study moors. Two parallel transects, 500 m apart, were walked through each square between 0600 h and 0900 h during June each year. Counts were conducted in the mornings, because previous work had demonstrated that passerine estimates were influenced by diurnal variation in detection rates (Thirgood, Leckie & Redpath 1995). All counts were conducted by the same observer in good visibility, light or moderate winds and no precipitation. The observer recorded the number of individuals (by species) within 200 m either side of the transect. Similar methods were used to estimate passerine abundance on the study sites where raptor foraging was examined in the summer.

Small mammal trapping

Estimates of small mammal abundance were obtained by snap-trapping in October and April each year. Two trapping sites were chosen in representative habitat in each of the six traditional grouse beats at Langholm (Figure 2.10). Four trapping sites were chosen in each of the other study moors, again attempting to be representative of each moor as a whole. In each site, 50 unbaited snap traps were set over two nights, giving a total of 100 'trap nights' per site. Traps were checked each morning and numbers of field voles, field mice, common shrews and pygmy shrews were recorded. Previous work had demonstrated that two nights of snap-trapping were sufficient to provide accurate indices of small mammal abundance (Redpath, Thirgood & Redpath 1995). Indices were also obtained in June on the study sites where raptor foraging was studied in the summer.

GROUSE MORTALITY

Kill searches

Estimates of winter grouse mortality on the 12 0.5 km² count sites at Langholm were obtained by systematic monthly searches for grouse carcasses between October and March using established techniques (Jenkins *et al.* 1963). During the first and last search of each winter, ten parallel transects were

walked at approximately 50 m intervals. In intervening months, searches consisted of six transects at 85 m intervals. Dogs were not used in these searches. Observers scanned continuously for feathers and bones throughout the transect and stopped and searched with binoculars at 100 m intervals. Grouse remains were classified as a carcase only if bones, flesh or primary feathers were present. A 25 m radius was searched around each carcase and any remains found were assumed to be the same carcase, unless obviously different. All remains, including flight and tail feathers, were collected and each carcase was marked with a small cane to prevent recounting. The following details were recorded:
- date of recovery and estimated date of death;
- grid reference and vegetation details;
- signs of predator such as pellet or scats; and
- grouse remains and whether they were intact or dismembered and plucked or bitten.

Field signs used to identify different species of predators were the same as those used by previous researchers (Jenkins *et al.* 1964; Hudson & Newborn 1995). Comparison of 49 grouse carcasses eaten by known predators revealed that it was straightforward to distinguish between grouse eaten by mammals and grouse eaten by raptors, based on an examination of the feathers. Raptors pluck feathers from the carcases, whilst mammals bite through the feather shafts. However, analysis of feathers and other features of the kills indicated that it was not possible to distinguish further between grouse eaten by peregrines and those eaten by harriers (Thirgood *et al.* 1997).

Radio-tagging

We captured and radio-tagged 130 grouse at Langholm in October 1994, 135 in September 1995 and 43 in March 1996, and monitored their subsequent survival. Grouse were captured at night in hand-held nets after dazzling them with a strong light. Each bird was aged, sexed and weighed and its wing length measured as an index of body size. All grouse were wing-tagged with small numbered metal tags and equipped with a necklace radio-transmitter. Radios weighed 15 g, measured 38 mm x 16 mm x 16 mm with a 250 mm whip aerial, and were attached with a cord around the neck (Kenward 1987). To find whether radios influenced survival, we caught 151 grouse in October and November 1993. In this test, all birds were wing-tagged and every alternate bird caught (N=73) was fitted with a dummy radio. We subsequently recaptured 31 of these grouse over the following year, of which 15 had tags and 16 had tags and radios. These results suggested no significant differences in survival between grouse with and without dummy radio-transmitters, although the statistical power of the tests to detect differences was low (Thirgood *et al.* 1995). Survival of radio-tagged grouse was monitored weekly and dead ones were located and examined to determine causes of death as above. Radio-tagged grouse were occasionally not found for several weeks until their carcase was located. In these circumstances, it was assumed that the bird died in the week following the date when it was last seen alive.

Worm burdens
Worm burdens of the parasite *T. tenuis* were estimated in the grouse which were killed by predators at Langholm. The total number of worms per bird was estimated by flushing the caeca with water, collecting the contents over a 210 μm gauze, diluting into 300 ml of water, and subsampling three times in 10 ml (Hudson 1986a). Average infection intensity was expressed as the geometric mean number ($\log_{10} x+1$) of worms per bird. These counts were conducted by Robin Foster.

RAPTOR NUMBERS

Breeding numbers and success of raptors
The numbers of hen harriers and peregrines attempting to breed were determined in early spring by systematically watching the moor from vantage points for displaying harriers and by visiting potential peregrine nesting sites for signs of occupancy. For harriers we also determined whether males were bigamous by watching how many females each associated with. The females were considered as either alpha (primary) or beta (secondary), depending on which of the two laid her eggs first. No case of males with three or more females was observed. Each female located during the spring was monitored through the breeding season to determine

clutch size, and the number of chicks hatched and fledged. In addition, checks were made regularly in all areas to make sure that no late breeders or relays were missed.

Numbers of raptors in winter
At Langholm we attempted to get a relative measure of how many raptors were hunting the moor by counting the numbers seen during routine fieldwork and during specific watches for raptors. The figures were expressed as the numbers of harriers and peregrines seen per 100 hours of fieldwork, and gave an index that was comparable between winters. The index did not distinguish between a small number of individuals seen repeatedly and a large number seen less often. It was difficult to assess accurately how many individual raptors were hunting a grouse moor in winter. For harriers, the numbers using nearby communal roosts could be counted, but, as birds can travel considerable distances, it was still not possible to say how many of them were hunting the moorland. For peregrines, the number of eyrie sites used as roosts could be estimated, but again it was not possible to determine where the birds were hunting. In addition, this procedure could not reveal the presence of any non-territorial birds.

RAPTOR FORAGING AND HUNTING SUCCESS

Raptor foraging
Observations on raptor foraging were conducted at Langholm during three winters (1992–93 – 1994–95) and three summers (1994–96). In each season, we selected a number of roughly 2 km² areas that could be easily viewed from a vantage point. Raptor watches were typically conducted for three-hour periods, during which time the entire area was scanned with binoculars at two-minute intervals, and the presence and behaviour of all raptors seen within the area were recorded. We attempted to distinguish between hunting and non-hunting raptors, based on their behaviour. For harriers we assumed that only those birds seen quartering the area were hunting, whereas any peregrine seen flying over the study area was assumed to be hunting. Perched raptors were also classified into hunting or non-hunting, depending on whether they

were scanning or involved in some other behaviour such as preening. With the exception of harriers in the summer, all raptors were recorded as the number seen per 100 scans. Each scan lasted roughly one minute. In the summer, areas were scanned as before but, when a hunting harrier was located, it was watched until it left the area, so for these birds data were recorded as the number of seconds hunting per hour.

Raptor hunting success

We collated information on raptor hunting success during systematic watches of raptors and routine fieldwork. For all raptors we recorded the number of strikes made at prey, the habitat in which the strikes took place, and how many of the strikes were successful. During the summer, we also recorded the time that harriers were seen hunting during raptor watches, and how many strikes at prey they made, thus enabling us to measure strike rate.

RAPTOR DIET

Diet was assessed in three ways:
• watches from hides placed near nests,
• analysis of pellets,
• analysis of prey remains.

Each of these methods was subject to its own biases. The most precise method for determining diet would be to watch hunting raptors and observe what they caught. However, this method was not feasible, given that raptors hunted over very large areas and, even when they were seen catching prey, it was often impossible to identify the prey species. Watches from hides placed near nests provided the least biased alternative, although some researchers have suggested that male raptors may eat very small prey items at the capture site and bring larger items back to the nest. This problem, however, was unlikely to affect the rate with which certain prey, such as grouse chicks, were brought to the nest. A more important constraint was that nest watches could be conducted only during the nestling stage and, because of the time-consuming nature of the work, only a small sample of nests could be studied in any one year. In order to obtain information from larger numbers of nests, and from times outside the nestling period, pellets and prey remains provided the most efficient source of information.

The principal bias in the analyses of pellets and prey remains was that large prey tend to be overemphasised. In prey remains, this could either be because small prey were less readily found in searches for remains, or because small prey were eaten whole, leaving no remains. In pellets, several small prey items often formed the basis of one pellet, but, unless distinctive individual features were present (eg beaks or feet), it was impossible to determine the number of individuals eaten. In contrast, large prey were more likely to form the basis of one whole pellet. Sometimes we were able to compare the results by testing one method against another. Almost certainly, however, data collected using the same technique at the same times of year were comparable between areas. There was little we could do about these biases, except to bear in mind the limitations they imposed on the resulting data.

Nest watches

At a number of harrier nests each year, we set up hides in order to record the diet. This work was conducted at Langholm and on other study moors. Once harrier nests were located, we determined hatch date mainly by watching the behaviour of the females. When incubating, food delivered by the male was consumed away from the nest, but once the chicks started to hatch food was brought back to the nest. At the hatch of the first chicks in each nest, we set up a hide 15 m from the nest and moved it closer over a period of three to five days until it was 5–7 m from the nest. Each nest was watched for up to 180 hours over a period of six weeks, until the chicks left the nest. We recorded the start and stop time of each watch, together with the number and age of the chicks, the time that any food was brought to the nest, the sex of the provider, and the type of prey. Where possible, prey were identified to species, but, where not, they were simply classed as passerines, small mammals, nidifugous young (such as grouse or wader chicks) and lagomorphs (rabbits or hares).

At Langholm we also set hides up within 15 m from three peregrine nests, one in 1995 and two in 1996. At each of these nests we recorded the same information.

Pellets and prey remains

Pellets and prey remains were collected at nests through the breeding season and pellets were collected at winter roost sites. We found no single, large communal harrier roost at Langholm, although we regularly saw birds roosting individually in tall vegetation. Harrier roosts near our other study moors had been located by others who collected pellets there through the winter. For peregrines, we collected pellets at a number of roosts in winter through searches every two months.

The analysis of harrier pellets was conducted by Roger Clarke. All pellets were dried, and any plumage and bill parts they contained were matched to a reference collection. Where too little plumage was present for easy identification, but downy barbules on the feathers were present, these were examined microscopically and identified to order, using the key of Brom (1986). More than one passerine of the same species in a pellet was recorded when more than one of the same bill part occurred; otherwise all the plumage in a pellet from a species was counted as one individual.

The count of small mammals in harrier pellets was taken as the minimum number, based on counts of skulls, jaws and teeth. Hair and bone occurring on their own were counted as from one individual. Small mammals were identified using the key of Yalden and Morris (1990). The larger mammals were identified by matching the medulla of guard hairs to the illustrations in Teerink (1991). Findings are presented as the percentage of pellets containing a particular species.

Peregrine diet was assessed mainly through the microscopic analysis of pellets. Peregrines regurgitate very few whole feathers in their pellets, so prey could only be assessed through the structure of feather fragments. Using this technique, it was not possible to identify species accurately, only to allocate them to taxonomic groups. Fortunately, the two main prey types, gamebirds (Galliformes) and pigeons (Columbiformes), were easily identifiable from feather structure (see Day 1966; Brom 1986). Other groups were songbirds (Passeriformes), waders (Charadriiformes) and ducks (Anseriformes). Within the gamebird group, it was not

possible to distinguish red grouse from other species, although it is unlikely that pheasant, partridge or black grouse were important prey items at any of the eyries studied.

Prey remains were usually examined in the field, and only unknown items were brought back for identification. Remains at eyries were buried to prevent recounting. The minimum number of individuals was recorded, based on the collections of body parts. For larger prey items, wings, feet or sterna were counted to give minimum numbers, whereas for small prey, such as meadow pipits, each pile of body feathers was counted as a separate individual.

Comparison of findings from different study techniques

During summer, pellets were collected from around harrier nests in order to compare the diet as assessed by pellet analysis and nest watches. Samples of 20 or more pellets were collected from 16 nests where hide watches were also conducted. We compared the proportion of pellets containing the four main prey types with the proportion of these prey as assessed from watches (Figure 2.11). Pellets tended to underestimate the proportion of nidifugous young, compared to nest watches, but not significantly so (Wilcoxon Signed Ranks Test T+=74, N=14, P=0.10). Passerines were underestimated by pellet analysis (z=2.16, N=16, P=0.01), whilst small mammals (z=2.05, N=16, P=0.02) and lagomorphs (T+=105, N=14, P=0.0001) were overestimated. These findings suggested that, at least in the breeding season, pellet analyses and nest observations gave comparable measures of the importance of grouse in the diet, though not the other main

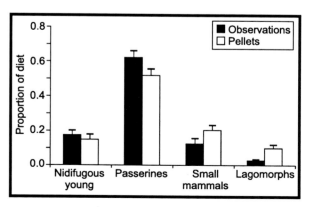

Figure 2.11 The proportions of the four main prey types in the diet of harriers during the nestling period, as assessed by pellet analyses and observations at 16 nests

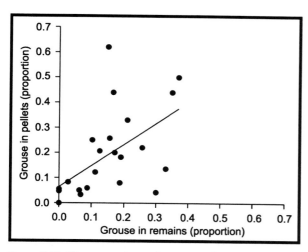

Figure 2.12 The proportions of grouse in the summer diet of peregrines as assessed by pellet analysis and prey remains at 24 eyries

prey types. Although the pellets from nests were likely to be predominantly from chicks, observations suggested that adults were eating parts of the same food items, so it was unlikely that diet varied between adults and chicks.

We also compared the proportion of grouse in the summer diet of peregrines, as assessed from pellets and prey remains. There was a significant linear relationship between the proportions of grouse in pellets and in prey items ($r=0.56$, $N=23$, $P=0.004$), and the slope of the line was not statistically significant from 1 ($t_{21}=-0.53$, $P>0.1$). This indicated that both techniques gave similar indices of the proportion of grouse in the summer diet of peregrines (Figure 2.12), although there was considerable scatter of points around the regression line, suggesting that some other factor may also be important. The watches from hides indicated that grouse formed 13% of 54 prey items, while prey remains from these eyries gave a figure of 14.4% of 105 items.

To summarise, comparisons between the findings from the different techniques gave similar overall estimates of the percentage of grouse in the diet of both harriers and peregrines. For harriers, however, mammals appeared to be overestimated and songbirds underestimated by pellet analysis.

HABITAT STRUCTURE
We obtained measures of habitat structure at Langholm for all study sites where grouse were counted and where raptor foraging was

monitored, and for the home ranges of a sample of 162 radio-tagged grouse. For the study sites, two 1 km transects were walked through the centre of each. A 2 m x 2 m quadrat was located along each transect at 50 m intervals, giving a total of 40 quadrats per transect. In each quadrat we estimated the percentage cover of heather, bilberry, rushes, grasses and bracken. We estimated the average height of vegetation in each quadrat and used a checker board of 50 cm width and 70 cm height, consisting of black and white squares of 5 cm x 5 cm, to estimate vegetation density in bands of 10 cm height. Density was measured by counting the number of squares on the board at each 10 cm height band that were totally obscured from an observer positioned 5 m south of the board with his eyes approximately level with the top of the board. The same observer collected all these habitat data.

Within individual grouse home ranges, we used the mean X and Y co-ordinates from all radio-tracking locations for individual grouse between October and March to estimate the central point for each bird's home range. Birds that provided less than five fixes were excluded, as were birds whose radios failed. When calculating the central point, individual fixes which deviated markedly from the rest were excluded. Typically such deviant fixes occurred during rare periods of deep snow cover, when birds flocked together. The central point was marked in each home range and four 100 m transects were marked along ordinal axes. Five 2 m x 2 m quadrats were located along each axis at 20 m intervals giving a total of 20 quadrats. Transect length was determined from an average home range size of 5 ha. Percentage cover, vegetation height and density were recorded as above.

CONCLUDING REMARKS
The above sections detail some of the background information to the Langholm and other study moors, and describe the various methods used to obtain the necessary information and the steps taken to validate the methods. The information will not be repeated in subsequent Chapters, but further details can be found in the scientific papers resulting from this work.

Chapter 3

Female hen harrier brooding chicks with a male in the background

3. *Factors influencing raptor numbers*

- The density of breeding harriers increased for up to four years following protection from persecution.
- The highest harrier densities occurred on moors where meadow pipits and small mammals (but not grouse) were most abundant.
- Small mammals were most abundant in areas of rough grassland, and pipits were most abundant on low-latitude moors. At Langholm, areas with more heather had fewer pipits.
- Harriers usually nested in rank heather at low altitude.
- Bigamy amongst harriers and male breeding success was positively related to grouse density.
- Peregrine nests were more widely spaced in the north of Scotland than further south, and their density was unrelated to grouse density.
- Overwintering raptor numbers varied considerably between different geographical areas. At Langholm, peregrine numbers were relatively constant between winters, but numbers of female harriers fluctuated in line with grouse density.

INTRODUCTION

In order to assess the impact of harriers and peregrines on grouse populations, it is necessary to understand how the numbers and diet of these raptors vary with grouse density (the numerical and functional responses). In this Chapter, we examine how the number and productivity of breeding raptors and numbers of overwintering raptors varied within and between our study areas over five years. Spatial variation in hunting patterns and diet of these raptors are examined in Chapters 4 and 5.

Numerous studies of raptors have found a positive relationship between breeding density and prey abundance (Newton 1979). This pattern holds both spatially, between different raptor populations, and temporally, within a population over several years with fluctuating prey supply. In Finland and North America, harrier breeding densities fluctuate in relation to the abundance of voles and other small mammals, which form their main prey (Korpimäki 1985; Hamerstrom 1986). Ratcliffe (1993) argued for a relationship between density and food supply in British peregrine populations, based on correlations between density and land productivity, and more direct evidence is available from other regions (Newton 1979). In terms of the impact of these raptors on grouse populations, we are interested in whether or not densities are correlated with changes in the abundance of grouse or other prey. If raptor densities vary independently of grouse, then their impact at low density could potentially be great, depending on the functional response.

In this Chapter, the analyses are conducted separately for harriers and then for peregrines. Our focus is on the relationship between these raptors and their prey, although we also consider the effects of human interference and nest site availability on their numbers.

HARRIER BREEDING NUMBERS

Several factors can influence the numbers of harriers which arrive on the moors to breed in spring. The three principal factors considered here are the availability of harriers themselves, together with suitable prey and nest sites. The number of harriers available to settle on particular areas each spring will mainly be influenced by the number of years that harriers have been allowed to breed there freely and by the number of harriers that have bred in the surrounding area, itself dependent partly on regional levels of illegal killing.

For all study moors, we had some data on hen harrier numbers for several years before the project started. At Langholm, there were no documented breeding attempts during 1980–85, but since 1985 harriers attempted to breed in each year (Figure 3.1). By 1996, five years after the start of the study, the breeding population had reached 14 females

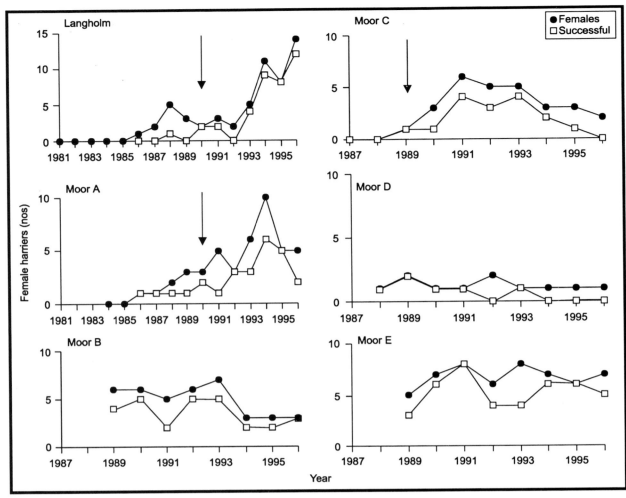

Figure 3.1 Numbers of female harriers attempting to breed (ie build a nest) and successful on Langholm and the other study moors in different years. Arrows indicate year when raptor nests were first protected

and eight males within the boundaries of the estate. Data from the other estate in south-west Scotland (moor A) also showed an increase in harrier numbers in the mid-1980s, as at Langholm (Figure 3.1). On moor C in Donside, numbers initially increased and then declined, on moor B (Perthshire) numbers declined between 1993 and 1994, whilst on the other moors numbers remained relatively constant, changing by one or two females each year.

Changes in numbers following protection

Changes in harrier numbers on these estates indicated that, once protected, harrier numbers initially increased. Densities of females and young produced from four estates, where we had sufficient data, indicated that numbers increased year on year for four years (years 1–4) following the initiation of protection (Figure 3.2).

Recovery time within estates may be influenced by the number of potential recruits

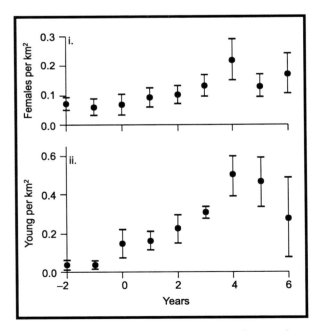

Figure 3.2 Relationship between the number of years of raptor protection and (i) the number of female harriers per km² of moorland and (ii) the number of young harriers produced per km² of moorland. Each point represents average densities from four estates. Raptor protection started in year 0

3. Factors influencing raptor numbers

Table 3.1 Numbers of male (M) and female (F) harriers attempting to breed at Langholm, the numbers of chicks tagged, the numbers (and percentage of the breeding population) of Langholm-born harriers that returned to breed, and the year in which they had been tagged

Year	Male	Female	Chicks tagged		Tagged harriers attempting to breed		Year tagged breeders born		
			Male	Female	Male	Female	1993	1994	1995
1992	2	2	0	0	0 (0%)	0 (0%)			
1993	5	5	9	8	0 (0%)	0 (0%)			
1994	8	11	16	7	0 (0%)	4 (36%)	M		
							F 4		
1995	6	8	18	11	0 (0%)	2 (25%)	M		
							F 2		
1996	8	14	20	23	2 (25%)	4 (29%)	M 1	1	
							F 1		3
Totals	29	40	63	49	2 (7%)	10 (25%)			

in the vicinity of the moor (Table 2.1). This may explain the rapid recovery at moor C, where the minimum number of young harriers reared within a 50 km radius was greater than at moor A and much greater than at Langholm from 1988 to 1992. Data from harriers tagged as chicks at Langholm suggested that the majority of birds attempting to breed came from elsewhere (Table 3.1). The first chicks were tagged in 1993 and in the following three years a maximum of 25% of males and 36% of females attempting to breed there were tagged. An indication of the distance that harriers are capable of moving from birth place to breeding place came from three birds that were marked as chicks elsewhere but subsequently bred at Langholm. Of these, one male moved 250 km and two females moved 115 km and 172 km.

Prey availability
Once harrier populations were protected from human interference, numbers took on average four years to peak. In looking for effects of prey availability on harrier nesting densities, therefore, we restricted ourselves to data from year 5 onwards. Red grouse, meadow pipits and small mammals (mainly field vole) formed 83% of identified prey items at the nests we studied (see Chapter 5), so we also restricted our analysis of the effects of prey densities to these three types. We examined male and female harriers separately because sexes vary in size and diet and because harriers can be polygynous.

Raptor densities are usually measured in two ways:
• as the average distance between the nests of nearest neighbours, or
• as the number of birds in a given area.

Both measures were related (ANCOVA controlling for year: females $F_{1,14}=14.2$, P=0.002; males $F_{1,14}=12.1$, P=0.004), but throughout this publication we have expressed harrier densities as the number per km² of grouse moor.

A comparison of harrier densities between moors indicated that densities of males and females were positively associated with meadow pipit abundance, and to a lesser extent with small mammal abundance (Table 3.2). In other words, harriers bred at higher densities on moors with large numbers of small prey. In addition, male densities were negatively associated with grouse density (ie more males occurred on moors with fewer grouse). Within moors, variation in male and female densities from year to year were again related to changes in meadow pipit and small mammal abundance.

Because meadow pipits and small mammals appeared to influence harrier density, it was crucial to find what determined their numbers. Meadow pipit abundance was estimated on 11 different grouse moors during the course of this study, plus two from a previous study (Redpath 1989). These moors included our six study moors, together with three others in the north of England, one in south-west Scotland and three in the Highlands. We have information

Table 3.2 Male and female harrier densities in relation to the abundance of the three main prey types. For each sex, two ANCOVA models were examined: between moors, controlling for year effects; and within moors, controlling for area effects. Log-transformed data were used for the analysis. Results given are adjusted sums of squares, the coefficient for the covariates, the F-statistic and the P-value

Source	df	Sums of squares	Coefficient	F	P
Between moors					
Males					
Red grouse	1	0.148	−0.164	6.32	0.022 *
Meadow pipits	1	0.576	0.835	24.61	0.000 ***
Small mammals	1	0.072	0.316	3.09	0.097 †
Error	17	0.398			
Females					
Red grouse	1	0.086	−0.126	2.70	0.118
Meadow pipits	1	0.507	0.784	15.86	0.001 **
Small mammals	1	0.163	0.473	5.09	0.037 *
Error	17	0.544			
Within moors					
Males					
Red grouse	1	0.002	−0.020	0.01	0.923
Meadow pipits	1	0.083	0.363	6.36	0.023 *
Small mammals	1	0.065	0.275	7.32	0.016 *
Error	16	0.208			
Females					
Red grouse	1	0.000	0.017	0.01	0.938
Meadow pipits	1	0.052	0.288	3.48	0.081 †
Small mammals	1	0.099	0.315	8.39	0.011 *
Error	16	0.239			

† $P<0.10$, * $P<0.05$, ** $P<0.01$, *** $P<0.001$

on the altitude and latitude of these moors, though no information on the precise habitat within these areas. We used three variables in a multiple regression model to explore the variation in average meadow pipit abundance:

- altitude of the count areas,
- latitude,
- grouse spring density.

Of these, latitude (coefficient=−3.95, t=−3.9, P=0.004) and grouse density (coefficient= −0.17, t=−2.32, P=0.046) gave significant negative relationships. Pipit abundance was not significantly associated with altitude. A stepwise model indicated that latitude accounted for 40% of the variation in pipit abundance, and spring grouse density a further 21%. Overall, the model accounted for 63.5% of the variation in pipit numbers ($F_{3,9}=5.22$, P=0.023). Thus, from our sample of moors, meadow pipits were more abundant on moors at lower latitudes and with fewer grouse.

Within Langholm moor, we examined 73 25 ha areas during the summer of 1996

(Chapter 2). In each of these areas we recorded the vegetation, altitude and the number of meadow pipits. Of the eight variables measured, only heather cover emerged as significant from a multiple regression model (coefficient=−0.003, t=−2.23, P=0.029). When examined in isolation, it was apparent that there was a weak but significant quadratic relationship between pipit abundance and heather cover (Figure 3.3, $F_{2,70}=3.48$, $R^2=9\%$, P=0.05), suggesting a reduction in meadow pipit abundance as heather cover increased beyond 30%. In other words, pipits were most abundant in areas that had a high grass/heather ratio.

Small mammals were trapped during the course of this study on six estates (Chapter 2). Trap lines were set so as to be representative of the main habitats and were classified into three crude categories:

- rough grassland dominant,
- heather/grass mix,
- heather-dominant.

We compared the number caught per 100 trap nights in spring between the different

                                   3. Factors influencing raptor numbers

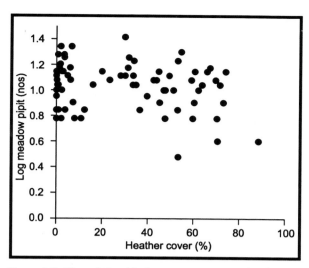

Figure 3.3 The relationship between percentage heather cover and the logarithm of the number of meadow pipits counted in 73 25 ha plots. The quadratic relationship $y=1.04+0.0039x-0.0001x^2$ was significant and suggested reduced pipit abundance in areas with high heather cover

moors and habitats. There were significant differences between habitats (log small mammals $F_{2,54}=5.79$, P=0.005), with the indices of abundance ranked grass>mix>heather. There were also significant differences between moors ($F_{5,54}=2.38$, P=0.05), with very few animals caught in any habitat on moor D. Differences between moors became non-significant (P=0.62) when moor D was removed from the analysis. As a general conclusion, it emerged that the two main prey species, which influenced the density of harriers, both benefit from a grassy rather than a heathery sward. The more the ground was covered with heather, the less the density of harriers was likely to be.

Nest sites

We studied nest site selection by harriers on three areas where we had detailed information on vegetation at nests and at sites at random locations (nests centred on Langholm and moors A and B). On these areas, 47 (94%) of 49 harrier nests were in heather, with the other two in rushes (Redpath *et al.* 1997). All nests were in vegetation over 25 cm (Figure 3.4), and a comparison of vegetation height at nest sites and randomly selected points showed that harriers selected taller heather than would have been expected if they had settled at random (nests 46.0±1.3 cm, random 27.9±2.0 cm, t=7.6, df=80, P<0.001). We next compared the altitude of nests at Langholm with the altitude of a random

sample of points that fell in suitable nesting habitat. There was no significant difference in altitude between the two samples (nests N=11, median=290 m; random N=25, median=280 m; Mann-Whitney Test U=200, P=0.92). Altitude, therefore, did not appear to influence nest placement, at least within the range of altitudes (120–570 m) available at Langholm. As our work focused on grouse moors, heather and consequent potential nests sites were generally abundant (see Table 2.1). This, together with the fact that harriers were prepared to nest in close proximity to one another (eg two pairs within 400 m at Langholm), suggested that nest sites were unlikely to be limiting on these moors.

Harrier settlement patterns

The choice of nest site is likely to be influenced not only by the vegetation at the nest, but also by the surrounding habitat. We therefore examined habitat selection on a broader scale to see whether harriers were choosing certain parts of the moor to nest. Using the habitat map based on the 1988 aerial photographs (Chapter 2), Langholm moor was divided into 164 1 km squares, and the proportion of heather cover and the occurrence of degenerate or rank heather was estimated in each. Heather cover was measured as the proportion of hectares estimated to contain >30% heather. From 1992 to 1996, harrier nests were found in 18 of these squares (Figure 3.5). Individuals

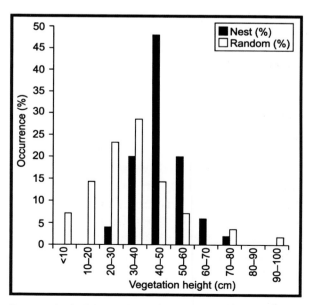

Figure 3.4 The height of vegetation at 49 harriers nests and at 120 randomly selected points on three areas combined

Figure 3.5 Distribution of 1 km squares used by nesting harriers on Langholm moor during 1992–96, in relation to the distribution of heather-dominant vegetation. Shading in the squares indicates the number of years that harriers attempted to nest in those squares, from one (white) to five (black)

known from their wing tags, that nested in more than one year, used the same square each time, so we have assumed here that the 18 squares were utilised by different individuals. We compared heather cover between these 18 squares and 30 randomly chosen squares (excluding those with no heather). Squares with nests contained a greater proportion of heather than expected by chance (nests N=18, median=0.79; random N=30, median=0.39; M-W U=595.5, P<0.001).

From the photographs, we estimated that rank heather occurred in 50 of the 1 km squares. As expected, from the harriers' nest site preferences, there was a strong association between squares used for nesting and the occurrence of rank heather (G=37.9, 1 df, P<0.001), with only one square containing a nest but no rank heather. A comparison of squares with and without rank heather indicated that heather cover was

more extensive in squares with rank heather present (with rank heather N=50, median=79.5; no rank heather N=30, median=17.5; M-W U=2566, P<0.001). A comparison of heather cover in squares with and without nests, including only those squares where rank heather occurred, revealed no statistically significant difference (nests N=17, median=84; no nest N=33, median=77; M-W U=789, P=0.29). Within these squares there was no difference in altitude between those with and without nests (nests N=17, median=305 m; no nests N=33, median=370 m; M-W U=399, P=0.18). So harriers appeared to prefer areas where rank heather occurred; these areas had extensive heather cover and occurred over a range of altitudes.

Use of the squares varied from one nest to nine nests in five years. Including altitude data for three additional nest squares which were just outside the habitat map, there was

3. Factors influencing raptor numbers

Table 3.3 Average size (mean±SD) of clutches and broods produced by three classes of female harriers at Langholm, 1993–96. Alpha and beta refer to primary and secondary females in bigamous relationships with a single male. The Kruskal-Wallis test was used to examine differences between the female categories

Female class	Nos of females	Nos of eggs	Nos hatched	Nos fledged
Monogamous	18	5.17±0.83	4.17±1.64	2.83±1.86
Alpha	11	4.73±0.86	4.27±1.05	3.18±0.39
Beta	11	5.00±0.43	4.64±0.98	2.54±1.30
P-value		0.34	0.66	0.57

a significant negative relationship between the altitude of the square and both the number of years used (log years $F_{1,19}$=7.48, P=0.013) and the number of nests found within it (log nests $F_{1,19}$=8.19, P=0.010). Although harriers nested at a wide range of altitudes at Langholm, areas at lower altitude were used more frequently.

Turning now to the timing of nesting, did harriers in each year lay their eggs earlier in areas where prey was more abundant? Using the date that the first egg was laid (estimated from known hatch dates), we considered the effect of the three main prey types (grouse, meadow pipits and small mammals) within the six Langholm grouse beats, plus three other variables:
• altitude in six 50 m bands,
• female age (1, 2 or 3+, estimated from iris colour),
• female status (in monogamous or bigamous relationships).

Both within and between years, altitude was the only significant variable in the model (within years $F_{1,30}$=4.32, P=0.046; between years $F_{1,29}$=7.46, P=0.011), with birds laying earlier at lower altitudes. Controlling for the effects of altitude revealed that age was significant ($F_{1,29}$=4.86, P=0.036), with first-year females laying at later dates. This indicated that harriers laid first at lower altitudes and that young harriers tended to lay after older birds. There was no clear evidence that harriers laid first in areas with relatively more prey (P>0.15).

HARRIER BREEDING SUCCESS
We next examined the influence of harrier density, breeding system (monogamy or bigamy) and prey abundance on harrier breeding success, measured as the number of young fledged (including nil values), within and between study areas. For six moors we had runs of data for over five years with no human interference. These included five of our study moors, plus one further area in Argyll (data provided by M Madders).

Harrier breeding system and density
We observed bigamous male harriers on 17 occasions during the study, of which 11 were at Langholm. On each occasion, these males mated with two females, with one of these females (the alpha female) being provisioned at a higher rate and laying her eggs before the second (beta) female. At Langholm we separated females into three categories:
• monogamous,
• alpha of bigamous male,
• beta of bigamous male.

Over the five years, none of the differences in the mean number of eggs or chicks per category was statistically significant (Table 3.3). This may be confounded by differences in prey availability between years and in different parts of Langholm moor. However, analysing within and between the beats of Langholm where harriers bred revealed no statistically significant differences in breeding success (ANCOVA controlling for area: for the three measures P>0.37; controlling for year: P>0.43). Moreover, from comparisons on different moors, and controlling for the effect of moor, female density had no apparent effect on the number of young produced per female ($F_{1,45}$=1.50, P=0.23).

Prey abundance
Harrier breeding success was examined in relation to measures of prey abundance within and between moors. In this analysis we excluded two records where human interference was suspected and seven further records where there were only one or two breeding attempts per moor. Within moors, the number of young produced by males or females was not significantly related to any of the prey variables (P>0.43 in all cases). Between moors, however, the number of offspring produced per male was positively related to spring grouse density ($F_{1,13}$=5.26, P=0.039, for other prey P>0.25),

Table 3.4 Numbers of occupied peregrine sites in early spring on each of the six study moors from 1992 to 1996

Area	1992	1993	1994	1995	1996
Langholm	3	3	6	6	5
Moor A	3	3	3	3	3
Moor B	1	1	1	1	1
Moor C	–	3	3	2	2
Moor D	1	1	1	1	1
Moor E	2	1	1	1	1

– No data

whilst the prey variables had no statistical effect on female breeding success (P>0.18). Thus, male harriers produced more offspring on estates with relatively higher grouse densities. As this was not the case for females, it implied that bigamous matings may be more likely on estates with more grouse, the production of males being dependent on the number of mates they had. We therefore considered the effect of prey abundance on the ratio of breeding male/female harriers from year 5 onwards. As grouse density appears to have a slight negative effect on male numbers, and this may in turn influence the male/female ratio, we included the numbers of males in the model (controlling for year: male harrier numbers coefficient=–0.12, t=–2.02, P=0.061; grouse density coefficient=–0.06, t=–2.05, P=0.057; pipits coefficient=0.14, t=1.73, P=0.10; small mammals coefficient=–0.06, t=1.73, P=0.54). In other words, our limited data suggested that in the study areas with more grouse, harriers tended to have more bigamous matings and this led males in high-density grouse areas to produce more young.

PEREGRINE BREEDING NUMBERS
Whilst harrier numbers on particular moors fluctuated more than two-fold from one year to the next, peregrine numbers were more stable from year to year (Table 3.4). Only at Langholm did the numbers of peregrines attempting to breed increase, whilst on two of the other estates numbers dropped by one pair over the five-year study. Peregrine densities were significantly different between moors (controlling for year: $F_{1,23}$=6.32, P=0.019), though differences between years within moors were not significant (controlling for area: $F_{1,22}$=0.16, P=0.69).

Peregrines are more obviously territorial than harriers, and their nest sites show a regular spacing pattern (Newton 1979; Ratcliffe 1993). Densities of peregrines on estates with no illegal control were also lower than those of harriers (Wilcoxon matched pairs P (one-tailed)=0.05 in all years). For comparison between areas, we therefore examined the spacing pattern of nests (used in 1994–96) in a region including the estate, but extending beyond the estate boundaries. As these peregrine nests were located in a wide area over a number of estates, human interference was suspected in most regions, although the extent was unknown. In addition to our study moors, we were also able to collect information on peregrines and prey in two other areas, one in the north of England and one in the eastern Highlands of Scotland. For relationships with prey between areas, we excluded the Islay population, because this was largely coastal, feeding partly on seabirds, and so not strictly comparable with the inland populations.

Changes in numbers following protection
Peregrines have been heavily persecuted in the past and it is likely that they continue to be shot and trapped in many upland areas. However, even on sites where they are shot, there are numerous recorded instances where killed peregrines are immediately replaced by new birds (Newton 1979; Ratcliffe 1993). This suggests a non-breeding element in the population, so that illegal control at current levels is unlikely to have a great impact on territory occupancy and nest spacing, though it might well reduce breeding success.

Prey availability
Moorland peregrines mainly eat racing pigeons and red grouse, though a wide variety of other bird species is also taken (see Chapter 5). Racing pigeons are mainly available during race days, when they can be super-abundant in peregrine territories for short periods of time. This makes them extremely difficult to count; consequently our discussion of prey availability necessarily focuses on grouse. As Ratcliffe (1993) pointed out, racing pigeon availability will tend to decrease northwards through Scotland, and we have therefore included latitude along with grouse density

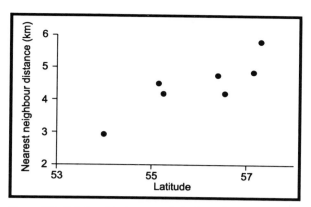

Figure 3.6 Relationship between latitude and peregrine density, as measured by mean nearest neighbour distance (km)

in the statistical models. There was a positive relationship between latitude and nearest neighbour distance between peregrine pairs over the seven study areas (Figure 3.6, r_s=0.82, N=7, P=0.024): the further north the study area, the further apart the peregrine nest sites. The relationship between grouse density and nearest neighbour distance was not significant (r_s=–0.25, P=0.52). After accounting for latitude, spring grouse density was still not significant (P=0.97). In other words, grouse densities had no obvious influence on the nesting densities of peregrines.

Nest sites

Peregrines show a distinct preference for nesting on cliffs, though in some areas they nest on steep slopes. The amount of nesting on low cliffs and on the ground has increased in recent years, as the peregrine population has expanded and all the most suitable cliffs in a region have become occupied (Ratcliffe 1993). Despite this, nest site availability may limit peregrine breeding densities in some areas where prey are abundant. In our moorland study areas, the availability of suitable cliffs varied, although remote, steep-sided valleys were fairly plentiful and peregrines used such sites to varying degrees in all areas. To get a measure of nest site availability in the different study areas, we examined 1:25 000 OS maps and noted the number of kilometre squares that had cliffs, crags, escarpments or quarries marked. As discussed above, nests tended to be evenly spaced, with the shortest average distance between nests, as measured by Ratcliffe, being 3.6 km, so we then measured the availability of potential sites within blocks of 3 km x 3 km. There

were considerable differences between areas, with the proportion of 9 km squares with crags ranging from 77% in one area of the Highlands to 17% around Langholm. However, there was no direct relationship between this measure of site availability and mean nearest neighbour distance (r_s=–0.14, P=0.73), suggesting that densities were not limited by nest sites as measured in this way. Those sites marked on maps were clearly preferred by peregrines, as they used them almost exclusively in those areas where their availability was highest (Figure 3.7, r=0.96, P<0.001). Where potential sites were relatively scarce, a higher proportion of birds nested on steep banks, unmarked on the maps, in sites such as sheep tracks or heather banks. In general, then, it appeared that peregrines in our study areas were not limited by a shortage of nest sites.

We thus conclude that peregrine density was primarily influenced by some correlate of latitude (perhaps racing pigeons) on our study areas, with more southern populations occurring at higher densities.

PEREGRINE BREEDING SUCCESS

Here, we restrict analysis to breeding attempts on our study moors where there had been no illegal control or clutch removal by egg thieves. There was no clear relationship between the number of offspring produced per breeding attempt and grouse density between moors (controlling for year: $F_{1,16}$=0.15, P=0.7), or between years within moors (controlling for area: $F_{1,16}$=1.54, P=0.23). Data presented by

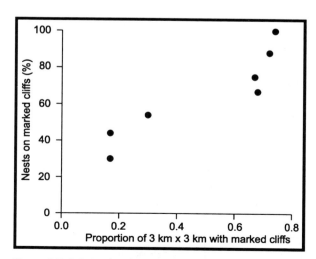

Figure 3.7 Relationship between proportion of 3 km x 3 km squares containing cliffs, escarpments or quarries and the proportion of peregrine nest sites at those features

Table 3.5 Peregrine breeding success (fledged young per female) in relation to grouse density and latitude. The number of breeding attempts excludes those where human interference was suspected

Area	Breeding attempts	Young per female	Spring grouse nos per km^2	Latitude
Langholm	20	1.76±0.15	30.5±1.4	55.1
Moor A	13	1.88±0.19	18.8±0.9	55.2
Moor B	5	1.60±0.71	6.7±0.9	56.4
Moor C	9	1.1±0.3	42.7±0.7	57.3
Moor D	3	1.0±1.0	22.9±3.3	57.3

Ratcliffe (1993) suggested a trend of decreasing productivity with increasing latitude, and this pattern was mirrored by the breeding success on our study moors (Table 3.5). This could have been either because of latitudinal climate trends affecting breeding, or because of latitudinal trends in prey availability.

WINTER RAPTORS

During the winter months, most bird species have migrated from the uplands, leaving grouse and small mammals as the main available prey for harriers in that season. Over four years, an average (±SE) of 88.7±9.6 hours were spent in fieldwork each month. Most harrier sightings at this time of year appeared to be of females. In total, 13 sightings of grey males were recorded in 2284 hours of general fieldwork, compared to 102 sightings of ring-tail harriers (juvenile males or females). If all harriers from the summer had stayed on the moor through the winter, we might

have expected a similar percentage of sightings of grey males (expected=16% of all sightings from data in Table 3.1 *versus* 11% of all sightings observed). However, it appeared that most sightings of ring-tail harriers were of females and not of juvenile males. This assessment was based on the fact that the size and plumage of closely observed birds indicated that they were females, and no juvenile males that were tagged as chicks at Langholm or elsewhere were observed there during winter. Within winters (Figure 3.8), raptor sightings did not vary significantly between months (controlling for winter: female harriers P=0.43, male harriers P=0.67, peregrines P=0.17). Between winters, numbers of female harriers varied significantly (controlling for month: female harriers coefficient=–1.89, t=–2.45, P=0.025), whilst numbers of male harriers (P=0.28) and both sexes of peregrines (P=0.97) did not. Overall, comparing sightings in each month over four years, peregrines were seen less frequently than female harriers (t=3.30, df=35, P=0.002).

Between winters, sightings of ring-tail harriers at Langholm varied almost five-fold. The numbers seen were highest (13.9 per 100 hours) in 1996–97 and lowest (2.6 per 100 hours) in 1994–95 (Table 3.6). There was a tendency for the number of harrier sightings in the five winters to vary in relation to grouse density (coefficient=0.81, t=2.77, P=0.07), but not in relation to October small mammal numbers (P=0.12), or in relation to the numbers of harriers present in the previous breeding season (P=0.12). Data on raptor sightings were also available from an area of upper Speyside from 1985 to 1988, and for an area in the Yorkshire Dales in 1987–89 (Hudson 1990). These data show that peregrines were more frequently seen in the Highland area, whereas harriers were seen more often at Langholm. Few harriers were seen in the Yorkshire Dales during the winters of 1987-89.

DISCUSSION

The numbers of hen harriers attempting to breed each year varied considerably both within and between study moors. One clear factor determining changes in breeding numbers over years within some of the moors was suspected human interference. Once

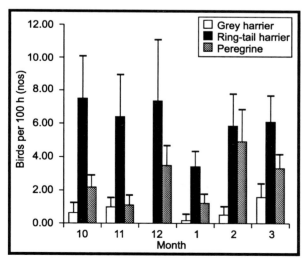

Figure 3.8 Changes in the mean numbers (±SE) of harriers and peregrines seen per unit time in each month of winter during routine fieldwork at Langholm. Data from four winters (1992–93 – 1995–96) combined

Table 3.6 Numbers of harriers (ring-tail only) and peregrines seen per 100 winter hours (October–March inclusive) at Langholm 1992–96 and in upper Speyside 1985–88. Data are also given for Langholm on the numbers of harriers and peregrines present in July (based on number of adult birds attempting to breed and number of young produced), grouse density in October (per 0.5 km²) and small mammal abundance (per 100 trap nights) in October

Area	Winters	Hours of observation	Nos seen per 100 hours		Nos in July		Nos in October	Small mammals per 100 trap nights
			Harriers	Peregrines	Harriers	Peregrines	Grouse per 0.5 km²	
Langholm	1992–93	373	9.82	2.81	4	8	24.8±3.3	4.0±1.8
Langholm	1993–94	335	6.30	2.66	27	9	23.3±3.0	8.2±2.5
Langholm	1994–95	809	2.61	2.12	42	18	22.9±3.2	1.9±0.8
Langholm	1995–96	641	5.19	2.67	43	21	20.7±2.8	3.2±1.0
Langholm	1996–97 *	123	13.86	2.44	65	24	26.8+2.4	11.3±2.5
Speyside	1985–88	395	4.30	6.08	–	–	–	–
Dales †	1987–89	577	0.50	2.2	–	–	–	–

* Data for 1996–97 based on October to December inclusive
† Data for Yorkshire Dales from September to April inclusive

protected, harrier populations increased for four years on average and, after this time, the numbers of meadow pipits appeared to be the primary factor influencing breeding densities between moors, though small mammal numbers also had an influence. Thus, moors with abundant small prey attracted high densities of hen harriers. Within moors, over the five years of the study, a similar pattern emerged, with harrier breeding densities varying from year to year in relation to changes in the abundance of pipits and small mammals.

Within our study moors, pipit abundance was related to latitude, with more pipits on moors in north-west England and south-west Scotland than further north. On different parts of Langholm moor, meadow pipits tended to decline as heather cover increased beyond 30% of the ground vegetation, suggesting a preference for grass or a mixture of heather and grass, as found by Coulson and Whittaker (1978). Small mammals were most abundant in areas of rough grassland and least abundant in heather-dominant areas. In other words, the highest densities of the small prey of harriers, and therefore of the harriers themselves, were likely to occur on relatively southern moors, such as Langholm, which also had a high ratio of grass/heather. This in part was likely to be a result of heavy grazing in recent decades.

Harriers preferentially nest in tall heather and their distribution at Langholm was largely restricted by this habitat. Although harriers nested at a range of altitudes, rank heather at lower elevations was used most frequently. In addition, harriers began breeding earlier at these lower-altitude sites in each year. We found no evidence that nest sites were associated with local abundance of the three main prey species. So, high numbers of pipits and small mammals attracted high numbers of harriers to Langholm moor, but, once there, harriers appeared to settle in relation to the availability of favoured nest sites.

The number of offspring produced by female harriers did not vary significantly with changes in the abundance of the three main prey species, either between estates or in different years on the same estate. We found no evidence that harrier density or mating system influenced the breeding success of females, though there was a non-significant tendency for alpha females in bigamous relationships to produce more offspring than monogamous females, which in turn produced more than beta females, as shown in earlier studies (Picozzi 1984; Simmons et al. 1986). Male harriers, however, produced more offspring on estates with more grouse, and this appeared to be related to the fact that on these areas males were more often bigamous.

Peregrine densities were more constant from year to year within areas, but differed greatly between areas. It appeared that latitude could account for much of this difference in density, with pairs being more widely spaced in the north, a pattern which may depend on reductions in racing pigeon abundance from south to north (a pattern supported by evidence presented by Ratcliffe 1993). There is little evidence of upland bird species (apart from meadow pipit, see above) decreasing in abundance with latitude within Britain (Hudson 1988). Data from our study areas and those presented by Ratcliffe (1993) suggest that peregrine breeding success may also decline northwards. Mearns and Newton (1988) showed that peregrine breeding success elsewhere in south-west Scotland was influenced by quality of nest site and spring weather. Those birds nesting in large cliffs tended to produce more offspring, whereas those in poor-quality, more accessible sites more often failed because of human or natural predators. On our areas, most sites were easily accessible and the availability of cliff sites was not related to latitude, so nest site quality was unlikely to account for latitudinal trend in breeding success.

Sightings of harriers and peregrines overwinter at Langholm were apparently not correlated with the numbers of adults present in the previous breeding season, or with the numbers of adults and young at the end of the previous breeding season. This was particularly so for harriers, whose breeding numbers varied to a much greater extent than those of peregrines. This pattern observed at Langholm implied that, within geographical regions, estates where raptors are killed during the breeding season may not necessarily have fewer raptors the following winter, and conversely estates which leave their raptors to breed may suffer no greater predation the following winter. To a large extent, these birds re-distribute themselves each year between breeding and wintering areas. At Langholm the availability of grouse and possibly small mammals seemed to influence the number of overwintering female harriers. This pattern was consistent with the finding that both grouse and small mammal densities influenced the hunting patterns of female harriers within winters (Chapter 4). As in the breeding season, sightings of harriers varied more between winters than those of peregrines, which tended to stay on territory throughout the year, leaving only in harsh conditions. Individual peregrines seemed more restricted to their territories, whereas harriers had more flexibility in their choice of wintering sites.

Winter raptor numbers differed considerably between those regions for which records were available. Peregrines were seen more frequently in Speyside than at Langholm, whereas harriers were rarely seen in Yorkshire. The low number of sightings in Yorkshire may be a reflection of the very low raptor breeding densities on these grouse moors (Gibbons, Reid & Chapman 1993), suggesting that, on a wide scale, breeding densities may influence overwinter numbers.

In summary, winter numbers of peregrines and harriers in different parts of the country may reflect differences in breeding densities, but there was no evidence that breeding densities at Langholm influenced subsequent overwinter numbers. At Langholm, it appeared that the abundance of prey, and in particular grouse, influenced the number of harriers seen per unit time each winter.

Chapter 4

Peregrine falcon in winter landscape

4. Factors influencing raptor foraging

- During winter within the study area, female harriers and peregrines of both sexes foraged primarily in relation to grouse abundance. Winter foraging was not influenced by habitat characteristics or by the location of roost sites.
- During summer, male harrier foraging was influenced by the location of harrier nest sites and was unrelated to either prey abundance or habitat characteristics. At this season, female harrier foraging was influenced primarily by the abundance of grouse chicks but also by long vegetation.
- Summer foraging by peregrines was unrelated to any measured variable.

INTRODUCTION

Hen harriers and peregrine falcons are highly mobile predators that inhabit a varied environment. Theory predicts that such species should concentrate their hunting in areas that give the greatest net returns of food quantity or quality (Stephens & Krebs 1987). Hunting success should be influenced both by the abundance of the prey and by the ease of capture. Thus, we might expect that harriers and peregrines would concentrate their foraging in areas with high prey densities where prey were easily caught. The ease of prey capture could be influenced by habitat characteristics, such as the height or density of the vegetation. At the same time, harriers and peregrines could be influenced in their foraging by the location of their nest or roost sites, particularly during the breeding season when they must return frequently to provision their young. An understanding of why harriers and peregrines forage where they do is critical to explaining the patterns of predation that we observed. In this Chapter, therefore, we examine harrier and peregrine foraging in relation to prey abundance, habitat characteristics and distance from nest and roost sites.

We investigated raptor foraging at Langholm over three winters (1992–95) and three summers (1994–96) by scan sampling a number of 2 km² areas of moorland from fixed vantage points. Observations were conducted between October and March on six areas in each winter, whilst during May and June we watched 14 areas in 1994 and ten areas in 1995 and 1996. On each area, we recorded the proportion of scans during

which a harrier or peregrine was observed and distinguished between foraging and non-foraging birds. We estimated the abundance of grouse, passerines and small mammals on each of the foraging areas, using pointing dogs, line transects and snap trapping respectively. Winter prey densities were estimated in October and summer prey densities in June. We surveyed the vegetation on each of the foraging areas, recording its height, density and the percentage cover of heather in 40 2 m x 2 m quadrats. Finally, we measured the distance from the centre of each foraging area to all harrier and peregrine nest sites. Further details of the methods used are given in Chapter 2.

WHAT INFLUENCES WHERE RAPTORS FORAGE IN WINTER?

We spent a total of 695 hours watching the six foraging areas over the three winters 1992–95. The average time spent on each area in each winter was 38.6±3.8 hours and the average duration of each observation period was 2.4±0.04 hours.

Female harriers

We restricted our analysis of winter foraging patterns of harriers to females, because male harriers were rarely seen on our study areas in winter (see Chapter 3). We examined the frequency of observations of foraging female harriers in relation to:
- the winter in which the observations were made,
- grouse and small mammal abundance,
- the height and density of vegetation, and
- the percentage cover of heather,
in a stepwise multiple regression analysis. We log-transformed the harrier, grouse and

Table 4.1 Stepwise multiple regression analysis of factors explaining variation in the frequency of observations of foraging female harriers in winter

Variable	Regression coeff	r^2	T	P
Constant	−4.82	–	–	–
Grouse log (x)	1.42	0.61	5.94	<0.001
Small mammal log ($x+1$)	0.26	0.70	2.18	<0.05

Significance of regression model: $F_{2,15}$=17.65, P<0.001

Table 4.2 Stepwise multiple regression analysis of factors explaining variation in the frequency of observations of foraging peregrines in winter

Variable	Regression coeff	r^2	T	P
Constant	−1.05	–	–	–
Grouse log (x)	0.36	0.25	2.33	<0.05

Significance of regression model: $F_{1,16}$=5.44, P<0.05

small mammal data and arcsin-transformed the heather data before analysis to ensure normality and homogeneity of variance. We did not include distance from roost sites in this analysis because we did not find a communal harrier roost. The regression model that best explained female harrier foraging included grouse density and small mammal abundance, which together explained 70% of the variation in foraging (Table 4.1). The positive relationship between female harrier foraging and grouse density accounted for 61% of this variation (P<0.001, Figure 4.1), and a further 9% of the residual variation was explained by the positive relationship between female harriers and small mammal abundance (P<0.05). Neither the habitat characteristics nor the winter in which the observations were made explained any further variation in female harrier foraging.

Peregrines

We adopted a similar approach to investigate the winter foraging patterns of peregrines. Both sexes were present throughout the winter and we could not always reliably distinguish between them, so we combined the two sexes for this analysis. We compared the frequency of observations

of foraging peregrines to:

- the winter in which the observations were made,
- grouse density,
- the height and density of vegetation,
- the percentage cover of heather, and
- a peregrine eyrie index calculated as the sum of the reciprocals squared of the distance to the six Langholm eyries, including those off the moor.

The data were transformed and analysed as for female harriers. The regression model that best explained peregrine foraging included grouse density, which accounted for 25% of the variation in foraging (P<0.05, Table 4.2, Figure 4.2). Neither the eyrie index, nor the habitat characteristics, nor the winter in which the observations were made explained any further variation in peregrine foraging.

WHAT INFLUENCES WHERE RAPTORS FORAGE IN SUMMER?

We spent a total of 665 hours watching the summer foraging areas during May and June over the three years 1994–96. On several occasions harriers established nests in the summer foraging areas. In these circumstances, we excluded these areas to avoid biases caused by harriers returning to

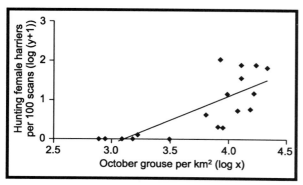

Figure 4.1 Relationship between October grouse density and winter observations of foraging female harriers at Langholm. Each point represents one foraging area in one winter. The data are log-transformed on both axes

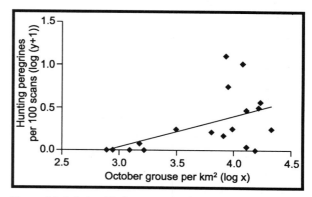

Figure 4.2 Relationship between October grouse density and winter observations of foraging peregrines of both sexes at Langholm. Each point represents one foraging area in one winter. The data are log-transformed on both axes

Table 4.3 Stepwise multiple regression analysis of factors explaining variation in the frequency of observations of foraging male harriers in May and June combined

Variable	Regression coeff	r^2	T	P
Constant	3.38	–	–	–
Harrier nest index log (x)	0.77	0.17	2.59	<0.05

Significance of regression model: $F_{1,32}=6.70$, P<0.05

Table 4.4 Stepwise multiple regression analysis of factors explaining variation in the frequency of observations of foraging male harriers in May

Variable	Regression coeff	r^2	T	P
Constant	3.32	–	–	–
Harrier nest index log (x)	0.82	0.13	2.22	<0.05

Significance of regression model: $F_{1,32}=4.91$, P<0.05

their nests. In total, we watched seven areas in all three summers, four areas in two of these summers, and five areas in one summer. The average time spent on each area was 19.5±0.5 hours and the average duration of each observation period was 2.4±0.04 hours.

Male harriers
We compared the frequency of observations of foraging male harriers to:
- the abundance of grouse chicks, passerines and small mammals in June,
- the height and density of vegetation,
- the percentage cover of heather,
- the summer in which the observations were made, and
- a harrier nest index calculated as the sum of the reciprocals squared of the distance to all the Langholm harrier nests,

in a stepwise multiple regression analysis. Data were transformed as above. The regression model that best explained male harrier foraging included the harrier nest index, which accounted for 17% of the variation in foraging (P<0.05, Table 4.3, Figure 4.3). Neither the prey abundance indices, nor the habitat characteristics, nor

the summer in which the observations were made explained any further variation in male harrier foraging.

The analysis presented above combined observational data collected during May and June. However, male harriers might have changed their foraging patterns when grouse chicks became available at the end of May (median hatch date of grouse chicks at Langholm was 28 May in 1995 and 30 May in 1996, see Chapter 7). In this case, male harriers might have foraged in relation to passerine and small mammal abundance in May and then switched to grouse chicks in June. Combining the data for the two months could in theory have masked any effect of prey abundance in the individual months. To test this possibility, we split the foraging observations into the two months and repeated the multiple regression analysis presented above. The possibility proved false, and in both months male harrier foraging was best explained by models that included the harrier nest index (P<0.05, Tables 4.4 & 4.5).

Female harriers
We also compared the frequency of observations of foraging female harriers in relation to the variables listed above for males. We initially combined the foraging observations conducted during May and June. The regression model that best explained female harrier foraging included grouse chick abundance and vegetation

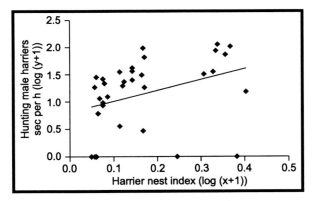

Figure 4.3 Relationship between proximity to harrier nests and summer observations of foraging male harriers at Langholm. The nest index was calculated as the sum of the reciprocals squared of the distance to all harrier nests, and so an increase in the index reflects increased proximity to nests. Each point represents one foraging area in one summer. The data are log-transformed on both axes

Table 4.5 Stepwise multiple regression analysis of factors explaining variation in the frequency of observations of foraging male harriers in June

Variable	Regression coeff	r^2	T	P
Constant	2.81	–	–	–
Harrier nest index log (x)	0.89	0.17	2.53	<0.05

Significance of regression model: $F_{1,32}=6.40$, P0.05

Table 4.6 Stepwise multiple regression analysis of factors explaining variation in the frequency of observations of foraging female harriers in May and June combined

Variable	Regression coeff	r^2	T	P
Constant	−1.94	–	–	–
Grouse log $(x+1)$	0.52	0.26	3.69	<0.001
Height	0.12	0.36	2.19	<0.05

Significance of regression model: $F_{2,31}$=8.84, P<.001

Table 4.7 Stepwise multiple regression analysis of factors explaining variation in the frequency of observations of foraging female harriers in May

Variable	Regression coeff	r^2	T	P
Constant	−0.12	–	–	–
Grouse log $(x+1)$	0.25	0.15	2.37	<0.05

Significance of regression model: $F_{1,32}$=5.61, P<05

height, which together accounted for 36% of the variation in foraging (Table 4.6). The positive relationship between female harrier foraging and grouse chick abundance accounted for 26% of this variation (P<0.001, Figure 4.4), and a further 10% of the variation was explained by the positive relationship between female harriers and vegetation height (P<0.05). The remaining prey and habitat variables, the harrier nest index, and the summer in which the observations were made explained no further variation in female harrier foraging. Because this analysis again combined data collected during May and June, we repeated the multiple regression analysis, splitting the foraging observations into separate months. In both May and June, female harrier foraging was best explained by regression models that included only grouse chick abundance (P<0.05, Tables 4.7 & 4.8).

Peregrines

The frequency of observations of foraging peregrines in May and June was examined in relation to the same prey and vegetation variables as harriers, the summer in which the observations were made, and a

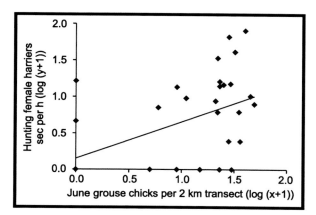

Figure 4.4 Relationship between an index of June grouse chick abundance and summer observations of foraging female harriers at Langholm. Each point represents one foraging area in one summer. The data are log-transformed on both axes

peregrine eyrie index calculated as the sum of the reciprocals squared of the distance to the six Langholm eyries. None of these variables explained any significant variation in peregrine foraging.

DISCUSSION

The winter diet of harriers and peregrines varies widely between areas, particularly between the uplands and lowlands. There is evidence that the importance of red grouse in the winter diet of both species increases with grouse density (Chapter 5; see also Watson 1977; Ratcliffe 1993). Raptors overwintering on grouse moors have a limited array of prey available to them. Many passerines and waders leave the uplands for the winter, moving to lower altitudes and latitudes. Moreover, as pigeon racing is largely confined to the summer, these birds are much less available to peregrines in winter. Pellet analysis revealed that grouse occur in up to 85% of peregrine pellets and 77% of harrier pellets collected on our study areas in winter, suggesting that grouse were important winter prey for both species (Chapter 5).

Given the above, it is not surprising that both female harriers and peregrines of both sexes foraged more frequently during the winter in areas of the moor which held the highest densities of red grouse. Having removed the effect of grouse density, female harriers showed further selection for

Table 4.8 Stepwise multiple regression analysis of factors explaining variation in the frequency of observations of foraging female harriers in June

Variable	Regression coeff	r^2	T	P
Constant	0.57	–	–	–
Grouse log $(x+1)$	0.48	0.16	2.43	<0.05

Significance of regression model: $F_{1,32}$=5.89, P<0.05

areas where small mammals were most abundant. We found no effect of any of the vegetation characteristics that we measured on the winter foraging distributions of either species. We know of no comparable research on the winter foraging behaviour of peregrines, while previous work on European and American harriers has concentrated on farmland and marshland where small mammals form the main prey (Schipper, Buurma & Bossenbroek 1975; Temeles 1986; Collopy & Bildstein 1987). We did not find a communal roost of harriers at Langholm, despite extensive searching and knowledge of a previous site. Solitary females were occasionally seen roosting in long heather and this behaviour may have been common. Winter foraging by female harriers was thus probably unaffected by the spatial location of roost sites. There was also no evidence that winter foraging by peregrines was influenced by eyrie location. Regular visits to eyries during the winter to collect pellets suggested that peregrines were not in continuous residence at all eyries. In an extensive review of the literature, Ratcliffe (1993) concluded that, whilst breeding peregrines have limited hunting ranges, non-breeders and breeders outside the breeding season often range widely to forage, citing examples of peregrines seen up to 20 km from eyries.

Harriers and peregrines have a wider spectrum of available prey in summer than in winter and are also more likely to be constrained in their choice of foraging sites by the need to return frequently to their nests with food. Correspondingly, we found a good relationship between the location of nest sites and the foraging distribution of male harriers. We do not know whether this relationship was due to individual males foraging near their own nests or whether harrier nests were in areas where males generally prefer to forage. However, evidence presented in Chapter 3 suggested that harriers did not settle where prey was more abundant, but where rank heather occurred at low altitude. Having removed the influence of harrier nest sites, we could find no further effect of either food or habitat on male foraging distributions. Furthermore, there was no difference in the foraging distribution of male harriers between May and June, before and after the period when most grouse chicks became available.

In contrast, female harriers were seen foraging more frequently in areas with high densities of grouse chicks and long vegetation. Surprisingly, we found no effect of nest sites on female harrier foraging distributions, suggesting that they may have hunted further from their nests than males. The sex difference in foraging may have been explained by the increase in grouse chick provisioning by female harriers during the latter half of the breeding season when the chicks could be left unattended for longer periods (Chapter 5). However, female harriers also foraged frequently in areas with high grouse densities during May before most grouse chicks hatched. It is possible that these harriers may have been hunting adult grouse, but we had few observations of harriers attacking adult grouse during the spring. It was difficult to explain why female harriers apparently preferred to forage in areas of long vegetation, as this would have provided better cover for prey. Perhaps long vegetation provided cover for foraging harriers to surprise grouse broods. There was no support for the idea that either male or female harriers preferred to hunt in areas with short or open vegetation.

Our results compare usefully with earlier work in Strathspey and Perthshire by Redpath (1992) who showed that, where grouse densities were lower than at Langholm, harriers hunted according to passerine distribution, but where grouse densities were higher than at Langholm, harriers hunted in accordance with grouse distribution. There are a number of possible explanations for these observations.

- Passerines occurred at approximately twice the density at Langholm as in Strathspey and Perthshire.
- There were differences in habitat between the three study sites.
- There were differences in scale between the two studies: the Langholm study investigated foraging distribution over an area of 100 km² with sampling areas of 2 km², whereas the Strathspey and Perthshire studies covered areas of 6 km², with sampling areas of 0.25 km².

- In the Strathspey and Perthshire studies, data for male and female harriers were combined, whereas in the Langholm study they were separated.

The lack of relationship between the summer foraging distribution of peregrines and any of the variables we measured was probably because, during summer, peregrines primarily fed on racing pigeons which we did not count. Furthermore, several of our peregrine eyries were located on the edge of the moor and these birds probably hunted extensively over the adjacent valleys.

Chapter 5

Peregrine falcon striking a red grouse

5. Factors influencing raptor diet

- Meadow pipits were numerically the most important prey of hen harriers during the breeding season. At Langholm meadow pipits formed 45% of prey items, whilst red grouse chicks formed 12%.
- Male harriers delivered most grouse chicks to nests on moors where grouse chick density was over 70 grouse chicks per km². If the relationship held true within moors, males would remove the highest proportion of grouse chicks at densities of 70 grouse chicks, or approximately 12 broods per km².
- Breeding status influenced the provisioning rates of grouse chicks by harriers, with both males and females in bigamous relationships catching more grouse. Female delivery rates were also influenced by brood size and grouse chick density.
- Racing/feral pigeons were numerically the most important prey species of the peregrine. At Langholm, pigeons formed 56% of summer prey remains, whilst red grouse formed 10%. Gamebirds were the most abundant prey type in pellets during the winter months.
- The proportion of grouse in winter and summer peregrine pellets, collected from a number of different eyries, increased with grouse density but levelled off at densities over 20 grouse per km². If the same relationship held at single eyries, a pair would have its greatest impact on grouse populations around eyries at grouse densities below 10 pairs per km².

INTRODUCTION

A raptor hunting over a grouse moor has a variety of prey to chose from. How often a raptor catches a grouse, rather than a meadow pipit or a pigeon, will depend on a number of factors, but especially on the abundance of grouse relative to these other prey. In this Chapter we focus on the relationship between grouse density and the number of grouse eaten by individual harriers and peregrines – the functional response. The numerical response was discussed in Chapter 3.

The shape of the functional response curve is important in assessing how the impact of raptors on grouse populations changes according to the density of grouse (see Figure 1.2). A linear relationship (type I) would suggest that the percentage of grouse removed by a predator remains constant at all grouse densities. An asymptotic curve (type II) would suggest that a greater percentage is removed at low densities, whilst a sigmoidal curve (type III) implies that a predator removes a greater proportion at intermediate densities. Studies of other generalist raptors have indicated that type II responses are the most common (eg Keith *et al.* 1977; Kenward 1986; Wikman & Linden 1981).

Our aim was to assess raptor diet across a range of grouse densities. Ideally, this would be done in the same areas over a number of years, under conditions of varying prey densities. However, in order to sample a wide range of grouse densities in five years, we collected data from a number of areas. Most of these were within our study moors, though some comparable data on harriers were drawn from the literature and some peregrine pellets were collected from eyries in the north of England and central Highlands.

This Chapter is split into two separate sections, on harrier and peregrine diet respectively. Within each section we assess diet in three distinct periods of year:
- spring (April–May), coinciding with the period when raptors are on breeding territory and laying or incubating eggs;
- summer (June–August), coinciding with the period from chick hatch to dispersal;
- winter (October–March).

In each species, diet was assessed using three different techniques: analysis of pellets, prey remains, and watches at nests from hides (see Chapter 2).

HARRIER DIET IN SPRING

Harriers generally settle on breeding territories in March. During late March and April, the males spend much of their time involved in display and courtship behaviour, during which time they feed their females. This means that males do much of the hunting at this time of year, and, because males rarely take adult grouse, most of the prey are small (small mammals and songbirds).

Harriers are susceptible to disturbance in early spring (Watson 1977), so we did not attempt to search for pellets around prospective nest sites, but relied instead upon observations of hunting birds and food passes. At Langholm, over 200 food passes from males to females were seen in spring during 1992–96 and all involved small prey. We also recorded a total of 68 strikes in April by harriers (34 successful), of which 88% were performed by males. A male was once seen to kill an adult grouse, which it ate *in situ* and did not attempt to carry to the female. Females were seen hunting occasionally in March and early April, and, of eight recorded strikes, three involved grouse (all unsuccessful), two at unknown prey, and one each at pheasant, curlew and common lizard. Once the females started incubating, and until the young were partly grown, all the hunting was by the males and, again, all prey items seen delivered by males were small. Over the five years at

Langholm we estimated that the median lay date was 27 April (ranging from 24 April in 1995 to 1 May in 1993).

HARRIER DIET IN SUMMER

Patterns in provisioning

During summer, hides were placed 5–7 m from harrier nests. Over the five years we spent 2614 hours watching 26 nests, including 22 at Langholm, two on Islay and two in the Highlands. Additional published data were available from the earlier work of Picozzi (1978) in Glen Dye in the eastern Highlands and of Redpath (1991) in Perthshire.

From the hides, we recorded how often the adult harriers brought prey, and where possible we identified items to species. Males often brought partly plucked prey to the nest and any that could not be specifically identified was placed in one of four prey types:
- nidifugous young (ie young of species such as grouse and waders that leave the nest soon after hatch and are characterised by long, strong legs relative to the rest of the body);
- small passerines (songbirds such as meadow pipit or skylark);
- small mammals (eg vole or shrew);
- lagomorphs (rabbit or hare).

Table 5.1 Summary of prey taken by hen harriers, from 2614 hours of nest watches at a total of 26 nests in three areas (Langholm 22 nests, moor B two nests and moor E two nests). Percentages are of all prey seen delivered to nests

| Prey type | Number (%) of items at | | | | | |
	Langholm		Moor B		Moor E	
Meadow pipit	946	(45)	65	(51)	22	(23)
Skylark	102	(5)	6	(5)	15	(15)
Other identified passerines	21	(1)	2	(2)	10	(10)
Unidentified passerines	260	(12)	27	(21)	7	(7)
Red grouse	261	(12)	0	(0)	2	(2)
Pheasant	2	(0.1)	0	(0)	15	(15)
Identified waders	27	(1)	3	(2)	5	(5)
Unidentified nidifugous young	36	(2)	0	(0)	8	(8)
Field vole	120	(6)	3	(4)	1	(1)
Rabbit/hare	44	(2)	2	(2)	4	(4)
Other identified mammals	11	(0.5)	0	(0)	0	(0)
Unidentified mammals	105	(5)	0	(0)	0	(0)
Other identified prey	7	(0.3)	0	(0)	0	(0)
Other unidentified prey *	159	(8)	18	(14)	9	(9)
Total	2101		126		97	

* Prey which could not be identified as passerines, nidifugous young, small mammal or lagomorph

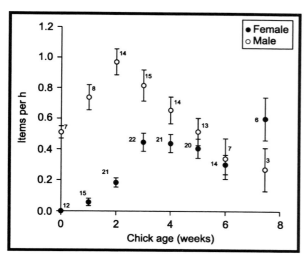

Figure 5.1 Relationship between the age of harrier chicks and the rate at which male and female parents brought food to nests at Langholm. Each point represents the mean±SE for a given number of nests. Data for males provisioning two females are given as a combined rate and data for chick age of 0 indicates incubation period

Items which could not even be classified to type were invariably small and were rapidly eaten. We were confident that most grouse chicks were identified from the hides during this period, from their characteristic pale-golden legs feathered down to the toenails.

Of the 2325 items that were seen delivered to nests during watches, 92% were identified to type and 73% to species (Table 5.1). The rate at which harriers provisioned their young varied with the age of the chicks and also with the sex of the parent (Figure 5.1). Males provisioned their females during incubation and for most of the first three weeks of the nestling period. After this time male provisioning rates declined and female rates

increased. On a daily basis, the first recorded delivery was at 0530 hours and the last at 2045 hours. Overall, provisioning rate increased up to 0700 hours, then remained fairly constant, with slight peaks in late afternoon and early evening (Figure 5.2).

A wide variety of prey was taken by harriers, from adders to full-grown pheasants, though most items were passerines (63%), with grouse forming 15% of items identified to species (for complete details of prey items, see Appendix 2). Of the 263 grouse that were seen being brought to harrier nests, 96% were chicks. Once the harrier chicks reached their fifth week of age, they started to leave the nest and spent much of their time in the surrounding vegetation. Some prey items were dropped away from the nest during this period and so fewer could be identified to type. In the first four weeks, 89% or more of items could be identified to type; in weeks 5 and 6, this figure dropped to 71% and 60% respectively (Figure 5.3). For comparisons within and between areas, we therefore used the data from nest watches in the first four weeks only (hereafter termed the early nestling period). In quoting Picozzi (1978), we included only those data collected during the first three weeks of the nestling period.

Adult females harriers were roughly 50% heavier than males and so were able to take larger prey. To compare prey between the sexes, we compared the proportions of large (nidifugous birds and lagomorphs)

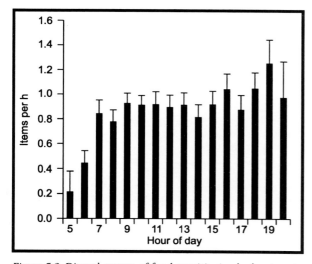

Figure 5.2 Diurnal pattern of food provisioning by harriers at Langholm. Bars indicate the mean number of items per hour±SE It was assumed that nothing was delivered during the hours of darkness (2100–0400 hours)

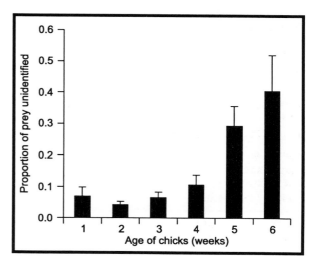

Figure 5.3 The proportion of prey brought to 26 harrier nests which could not be identified to type. Data are given by week as mean+SE

Table 5.2 The number of small and large prey that were seen to be delivered to harrier nests by males and females in the early nestling period

Nest	Males Small	Males Large	Females Small	Females Large	G-statistic (1 df)	P
1	49	3	14	11	15.8	<0.001
2	52	12	29	11	1.1	NS
3	31	3	21	17	12.5	<0.001
4	16	5	14	8	0.8	NS
5	59	2	66	11	5.4	<0.05
6	57	3	57	9	2.8	NS
7	80	9	19	8	5.5	<0.05
8	99	13	49	9	0.5	NS
9	29	11	16	9	0.5	NS
10	27	2	10	18	22.8	<0.001
11	30	12	13	18	6.4	<0.05
12	19	4	12	14	7.3	<0.01
13	47	14	20	7	0.1	NS
14	18	2	8	12	11.9	<0.001
15	20	6	14	17	6.1	<0.05
Total	777	114	385	187	82.6	<0.001

NS Not significant

versus small items (passerines and small mammals) taken by each sex for each nest where we had identified more than 20 items per sex (Table 5.2). Females brought in a greater proportion of large prey than males at all nests (overall % large prey: females 32%, males 13%), and these differences were significant at nine of the 15 nests, and overall.

The percentage of grouse in the diet of male and female harriers did not vary significantly over the early nestling period (controlling for the effects of year: males $F_{1,11}$=0.01, P=0.9; females $F_{1,7}$=2.29, P=0.17). Within weeks, data were pooled for males and females, due to small sample sizes at individual nests. Weeks when fewer than ten prey items were observed were excluded from analyses.

Table 5.3 Comparison of provisioning rates at harrier nests where the male was monogamous or bigamous. Data given as means per nest±1SE. For bigamous males, rates given per alpha (α) and beta (β) female and as the overall rate per male (combining rates to α and β females)

Type		N	Male	Items per h Female	Total
Monogamous		8	0.80±0.08	0.41±0.09	1.21
Bigamous	α	8	0.62±0.06	0.28±0.03	0.90
	β	6	0.32±0.07	0.31±0.02	0.63
	Overall	6	0.94±0.11		

Harrier breeding system and provisioning rate between nests

Over four years at Langholm, we watched eight nests where the male was monogamous and 14 nests where the male was bigamous. A comparison of provisioning rates between these nests in the early nestling period (Table 5.3) revealed significant differences for males ($F_{2,19}$=12.79, P<0.001), with monogamous birds provisioning at greater rates per nest. The differences were not significant for females ($F_{2,19}$=1.20, P=0.32). Bigamous males delivered the same number of items per hour as monogamous males, but divided them between two nests. However, females mated to bigamous males received significantly fewer items than females mated to monogamous males ($F_{2,19}$=8.81, P=0.002). Despite this, there were no significant differences in fledging success between the classes of females (Chapter 3). One likely reason why brood sizes were not reduced in nests of bigamous males was that the females, and to a lesser extent the males, brought in larger prey, thus partly compensating for the reduced provisioning rate (Table 5.4).

Prey abundance and provisioning rates – functional responses

Because prey varied between the sexes, we considered relationships between prey type and provisioning rates for males and females separately in the early nestling period. We investigated how provisioning rates varied in relation to the local abundance of grouse, meadow pipits and small mammals (Figure 5.4). Before testing for significance, we log-transformed provisioning rate. In all cases there was a tendency for both male and

Table 5.4 Comparison of prey sizes delivered by male and female harriers to nests in which the male was monogamous or bigamous. Nests of bigamous birds were divided into alpha (α) and beta (β), according to lay date, and prey were divided into large (nidifugous and lagomorphs) and small (passerines and small mammals)

Nest type		Males Small	Males Large	Males % large	Females Small	Females Large	Females % large
Monogamous		325	39	11	208	46	18
Bigamous	α	196	44	18	93	52	36
	β	96	13	12	53	64	55
G-statistic		7.21			51.4		
P		<0.05			<0.001		

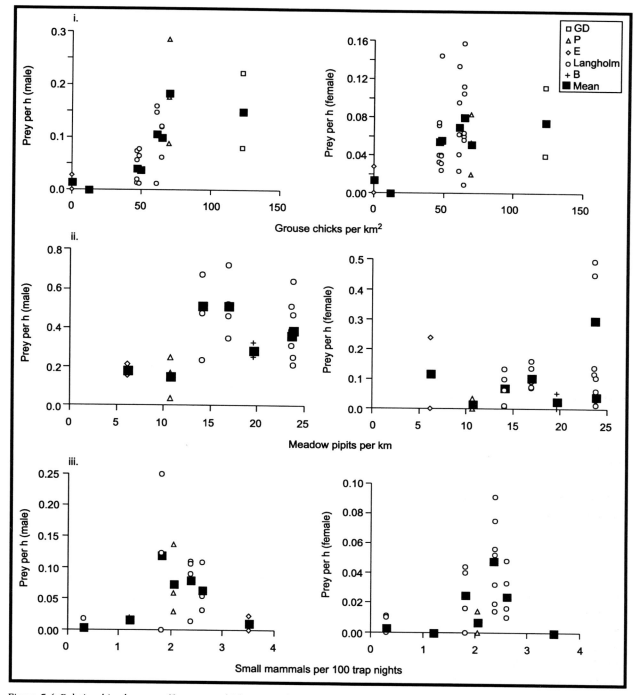

Figure 5.4 Relationships between (i) rates at which grouse chicks were brought to harrier nests and grouse chick density (per km²), (ii) rates at which meadow pipits were brought to harrier nests and meadow pipit abundance (per km) and (iii) rates at which small mammals were brought to harrier nests and small mammal abundance (per 100 trap nights). Each point indicates a separate nest and the symbols indicate different study areas. Filled squares indicate means for each year. GD refers to Glen Dye (Picozzi 1978); moor P represents data from a Perthshire moor in 1988 (Redpath 1991)

female harriers to have higher delivery rates of specific prey when these prey were more common. The relationships were significant for both sexes of harriers and grouse chicks (males r=0.67, N=24, P<0.001; females r=0.53, N=31, P=0.002) and also for male harriers and pipits (r=0.45, N=22, P=0.038) and female harriers and small mammals (r=0.52, N=29, P=0.004). The other relationships were not quite significant (males and small mammals

r=0.41, N=22, P=0.06; females and pipits r=0.26, N=29, P=0.17).

The relationship between grouse chick density and male provisioning (Figure 5.4i) appeared to be s-shaped, or sigmoidal, with a sharp increase in provisioning of grouse between densities of 50 and 70 grouse chicks per km². No such pattern was obvious for the other relationships, although the ability to

Table 5.5 Outputs from a stepwise multiple regression model, examining variation in the provisioning rate of grouse chicks by male (N=22) and female (N=29) harriers. The dependent variable was the delivery rate of grouse chicks to the nest (log) and the independent variables were grouse chick density, meadow pipit abundance, small mammal abundance, and breeding status (monogamous or bigamous), hatch date and the brood size of the harriers. Only significant relationships are shown

Males Variable	Coefficient	t	R^2	Cumulative R^2 (%)
Grouse chicks	0.016	4.79	53.5	53.5
Status	0.330	2.22	9.5	63.0

Females Variable	Coefficient	t	R^2	Cumulative R^2 (%)
Status	0.290	4.19	39.4	39.4
Brood size	0.194	3.54	19.7	59.1
Grouse chicks	0.007	2.98	10.7	69.8

detect such patterns was reduced by small sample sizes.

Explaining variation in the provisioning rate of grouse chicks

There was considerable variation in the rate with which male and female harriers delivered grouse chicks to nests in the early nestling period. To try and explain some of this variation, we used a stepwise multiple regression model, with grouse delivery rates (log-transformed) as the dependent variable. As independent variables, we used the prey density estimates, hatch date, chick number and status (measured as monogamous, alpha and beta for females and monogamous or bigamous for males). We excluded data from Picozzi's study, because he gave no measure of pipit or small mammal abundance. For

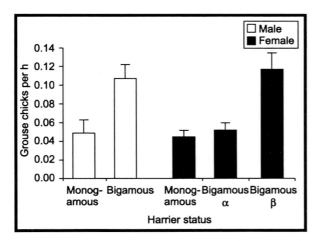

Figure 5.5 Relationship between the mean rate (±SE) at which grouse chicks were delivered to nests and harrier breeding status, defined as monogamous, alpha bigamous or beta bigamous. Data are presented separately for males and females

males (N=22), grouse chick density accounted for 53% of the variation in provisioning of grouse, with male status accounting for a further 9% (Table 5.5). None of the other variables contributed significantly to the model. For females (N=29), status accounted for 39% of the variation, with the number of harrier chicks in the nest accounting for a further 20% and grouse chick density 11%.

Those findings suggested that for male harriers the number of grouse chicks killed in the early nestling period was influenced primarily by the abundance of grouse chicks and, to a lesser extent, by the status of the male (Table 5.5). Male predation rates on grouse chicks were therefore expected to be highest on areas where grouse were abundant and when the males were bigamous. For females, the number of grouse killed was primarily influenced by status, with beta females taking the most grouse (Figure 5.5), but also by the number of chicks in the nest (more grouse delivered to nests with more harrier chicks), and the density of grouse chicks (more grouse delivered at higher grouse chick density).

HARRIER DIET IN WINTER

In winter, male harriers tended to leave the grouse moors for the lowlands, as did their small bird prey species. Many female harriers continued to hunt the moors through the winter, as they were able to catch the larger prey (grouse and lagomorphs) which remained year-round in this habitat. Pellets collected from roosts used by more female harriers than males revealed a higher proportion of large prey (Marquiss 1980). With the help of RSPB and Raptor Study Group members, we obtained pellets from upland roost sites in six areas around Scotland and the north of England (Table 5.6). We found no large communal roost site at Langholm, although we managed to collect sufficient pellets from occasionally used sites just off the main moor in the winter of 1995–96. These pellets suggested that the harriers using these roost sites mostly foraged away from the moorland, because species such as linnet and brambling predominated.

The proportions of main prey in the pellets varied between locations (Table 5.6). For each roost area, we estimated the abundance

Table 5.6 Contents of harrier pellets collected from upland roost sites in winter

| Area | Years | Nos of pellets | Red grouse abundance per km² † | % pellets containing | | | |
				grouse	passerines	small mammals	lagomorphs
Inverness-shire	86–88	164	2.8	18	79	12	3
Perthshire	90–94	200	3.1	31	19	14	40
Ayrshire	92–93	42	5.0	71	14	14	2
Dumfries-shire 1	94–95	27	14.6	11	85	0	7
Dumfries-shire 2 *	95–96	30	2.9	3	23	67	0
Lancashire	92–93	56	39.8	54	7	30	0

* Langholm

† Grouse abundance is given per km² and was calculated as the product of October counts and the proportion of heather moorland within 5 km of the roost

of grouse, based on October grouse counts on the nearest grouse moor multiplied by the amount of heather-dominant vegetation within a 5 km radius of the roost site. Where pellets were collected from more than one roost site in one area, we used a central point between the roost sites. On average, grouse were found in 31% of all pellets, although there was no clear relationship between the percentage of pellets containing grouse and local grouse density ($r_s=0.54$, N=6, P=0.26).

PEREGRINE DIET IN SPRING

The number of peregrine pellets collected varied considerably between eyries, and in any one year we excluded data from eyries that yielded fewer than ten pellets. Over the five years, during April and May, we collected 420 peregrine pellets from 17 eyries on seven estates (Table 5.7). We examined how the proportion of peregrine pellets containing gamebirds varied in relation to grouse density and latitude. In

contrast to harriers which nested on the heather moorland, many peregrine eyries were situated up to several kilometres away from moorland. Therefore, rather than give grouse densities by moor, we estimated the number of grouse within a 2 km radius from the eyrie, by multiplying the proportion of the area covered in heather-dominant moor with the grouse density for that moor; 2 km was selected as being approximately half the overall nearest neighbour distance and the area of heather-dominant moorland was estimated by marking the habitat on to maps in the field. Some keepers had erected dovecotes near to certain eyries so these eyries were excluded from the analyses to prevent the potential confounding effect of increased pigeon abundance. Pellets were collected from some eyries in more than one year. To minimise the problem of inter-dependence between data points, we used annual average values for these eyries in the analyses.

Table 5.7 Prey items in peregrine pellets classed as four main prey groups, representing gamebirds (Galliformes), pigeons (Columbiformes), waders (Charadriiformes) and passerines (Passeriformes). Data from all eyries and all years pooled. Some pellets contained more than one item, so percentages add up to more than 100

| Season | Area | Nos of pellets | % pellets containing | | | |
			Galliformes	Columbiformes	Charadriiformes	Passeriformes
Spring	N England	123	49	53	15	18
	SW Scotland	166	17	61	9	23
	Highlands	131	40	46	12	30
	Total	420	34	54	12	24
Summer	N England	233	30	85	22	51
	SW Scotland	487	16	73	18	41
	Highlands	401	36	48	10	15
	Total	1133	26	67	16	34
Winter	N England	569	54	44	22	36
	SW Scotland	404	46	31	11	33
	Total	973	51	40	17	35

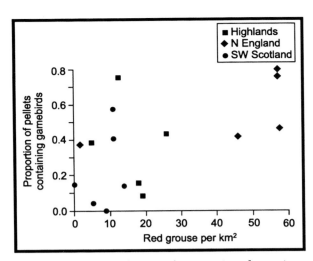

Figure 5.6 Relationship between the proportion of peregrine pellets containing gamebirds and red grouse abundance (per km²) in spring (April–May). Each point represents one eyrie and symbols indicate the region where pellets were collected

In all analyses, we initially tested for a linear relationship, to see whether the proportion of grouse in the pellets increased with increasing grouse numbers around the nest. We then tested for a quadratic relationship (forced through the origin) to determine whether or not there was any evidence of curvilinearity. Where the data showed curvilinearity, we used a simple Michaelis-Menton model to fit a line through the data. This line was fitted based on the reasoning that the proportion of pellets containing gamebirds should increase from the origin, but level out at high grouse densities. Finally, within the linear and quadratic relationships, we checked whether latitude could account for any of the residual variation. For the purpose of these analyses, we assumed that pellets provided a reasonable index of the rate of predation on grouse, which was consistent between eyries and within seasons.

The percentage of pellets containing gamebirds in spring was almost 80 at eyries where grouse were abundant, and overall there was a positive linear relationship ($F_{1,14}$=6.46, P=0.024) between grouse abundance and the proportion of pellets containing gamebirds (Figure 5.6). When latitude was included in this model, it had no significant effect (t=–0.1, P=0.92). A model forced through the origin and incorporating a quadratic term provided no evidence for curvilinearity in the spring data (t=–1.44, P=0.17).

PEREGRINE DIET IN SUMMER

Pellet analysis
As for spring diet, grouse abundance was estimated using April density per count site multiplied by the proportion of heather-dominant moorland within a 2 km radius of the eyrie. We again excluded data from eyries where fewer than ten pellets were collected, and from eyries with dovecotes placed nearby. In summer, we collected 1133 pellets from 30 eyries on 12 estates (Table 5.7).

These data revealed a significant linear relationship between the proportion of summer pellets containing gamebirds and grouse abundance (Figure 5.7i, $F_{1,26}$=5.2, P=0.031). Latitude in this analysis was not significant (t=1.43, P=0.16). There was evidence of curvilinearity in this relationship (t=–2.25, P=0.033) and latitude in the quadratic model was close to significance (t=1.93, P=0.065).

Prey remains analysis
In total we collected 876 prey items from 20 eyries on six estates. The bulk of these items

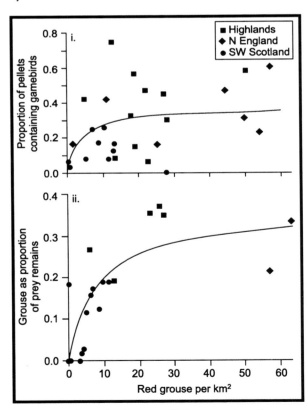

Figure 5.7 Relationship between (i) the proportion of peregrine pellets containing gamebirds and grouse abundance (numbers per km²) collected in summer (June–September) and (ii) the proportion of grouse in peregrine prey remains and grouse abundance (per km²) in summer (June–September). Each point represents one eyrie and symbols indicate the region where pellets were collected

Table 5.8 Peregrine prey items collected during summer from 20 eyries in three regions. Prey items are listed by numerical importance

Number of eyries	13	2	5
Species	SW Scotland	North England	Highlands
Racing/feral pigeon	335	24	64
Red grouse	63	14	53
Meadow pipit	34	1	10
Starling	35	4	2
Skylark	23	0	2
Corvid sp.	5	0	16
Black-headed gull	10	0	10
Unidentified passerine	16	0	4
Carrion/hooded crow	8	0	8
Golden plover	10	1	3
Rook	9	0	5
Curlew	9	0	4
Lapwing	10	0	2
Song thrush	8	2	0
Snipe	7	0	0
Thrush sp.	5	0	2
Jackdaw	3	0	4
Mistle thrush	3	1	1
Oystercatcher	3	0	1
Magpie	3	1	1
Wood pigeon	1	0	3
Ring ouzel	1	1	2
Mountain hare	0	0	2
Woodcock	2	0	0
Chaffinch	2	0	0
Blackbird	2	0	0
Pheasant	1	1	0
Common gull	0	0	2
Black grouse	1	0	1
Redshank	0	1	0
Rabbit	0	0	1
Siskin	1	0	0
Mallard	1	0	0
Jay	0	0	1
Kestrel	1	0	0
Common tern	0	0	1
Great spotted woodpecker	0	1	0
Ptarmigan	0	0	1
Raven	1	0	0

consisted of racing and feral pigeons (48%), with red grouse being the second most abundant item (Table 5.8). Of the 129 gamebirds collected, 96% were red grouse, suggesting that, at least in summer, the vast majority of pellets containing Galliformes would have contained red grouse. Of the grouse collected, the majority were adult (92%), though the remains of ten chicks were also collected. There was a significant linear relationship between the proportion of grouse in the remains at eyries during the summer and April grouse abundance (Figure 5.7ii, $F_{1,17}$=11.04, P=0.004). Latitude was significant when included in the linear model (t=4.53, P<0.001). Again, there was evidence for curvilinearity in the data (t=−6.42, P<0.001), but latitude was not significant in this model (t=1.05, P=0.31).

Prey remains can be used to estimate the percentage of grouse in the diet by biomass (see Chapter 6 for estimates of prey weight). As a percentage of prey items, grouse were estimated to form 16.9% by number and 27.1% by biomass. There was a good linear relationship between the two measures ($F_{1,18}$=48.8, P<0.001). Because peregrine breeding success did not vary with grouse density (Chapter 3) and therefore the biomass requirements of broods were unlikely to vary widely between areas, the percentage of prey items consisting of grouse probably gave a reasonable indication of how the number of grouse killed by peregrines varied with grouse density.

PEREGRINE DIET IN WINTER
During winter (October–March), we collected 849 pellets from 15 eyries on five estates (Table 5.7). At this time of year, there was no pigeon racing and gamebirds became more important in the diet. As October grouse density was not available for all areas, we used the July density minus the number shot per km² of grouse moor to assess the effect of autumn grouse abundance on winter diet. At Langholm, we had measures of July numbers per km², number shot per km² and October numbers per km² for the six grouse beats on the moor over five years. The slope of the relationship between October numbers and July numbers minus the number shot per km² was not significantly different between years ($F_{4,20}$=0.34, P=0.85) or between areas ($F_{5,18}$=1.21, P=0.34), and after pooling all data a significant linear relationship emerged. This indicated that July numbers per km² minus the number shot per km² gave a reasonable estimate of grouse availability in October at Langholm, and we used this relationship to calculate October densities on the other moors.

The proportion of pellets containing gamebirds increased as the estimated October abundance of grouse increased (Figure 5.8, $F_{1,11}$=9.43, P=0.011). Latitude was not quite significant in the model (t=1.89, P=0.088). There was evidence for curvilinearity in this relationship (t=−2.37, P=0.037), and latitude

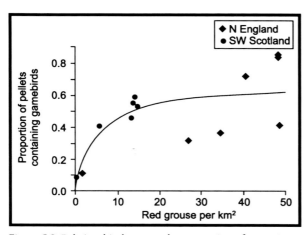

Figure 5.8 Relationship between the proportion of peregrine pellets that contained gamebirds and grouse abundance (per km²) in winter (October–March). Each point represents one eyrie and symbols indicate the region where pellets were collected

was not significant when included in the quadratic model (t=1.66, P=0.128). Using July grouse density, rather than estimated October densities, gave similar results (linear $F_{1,11}$=6.64, P=0.026; quadratic t=−2.33, P=0.04). In other words, individual peregrines took more grouse in winter as grouse densities increased.

DISCUSSION

Both harriers and peregrines ate a wide variety of prey species. In summer, we recorded 35 prey species at harrier nests and 36 prey species at peregrine nests. However, the majority of items were from just two or three species: meadow pipits and grouse were the main prey of harriers, and pigeons and grouse were the main prey of peregrines. For neither raptor species was red grouse numerically the most important prey.

A comparison of provisioning rates between nests indicated that the rate at which male harriers delivered grouse and meadow pipits to their nests increased as these respective prey densities rose. Clearly, we might expect the provisioning rate of any one prey species to increase in relation to its density, but the shape of the relationship was important in judging whether harriers actively responded to changes in the density of that prey, or were merely coming across more of them by chance. Although sample sizes were small, the relationship between male provisioning and grouse chick density was the only one which appeared to be sigmoidal (s-shaped), suggesting that males switched their hunting

patterns to search for grouse in years when grouse became more available. This idea was supported by the observations of Redpath (1992), who found that harriers hunted the habitats utilised by passerines when grouse were scarce, but hunted habitats preferred by grouse when grouse were abundant. The shape of this relationship suggested that, at grouse chicks densities up to 70 per km², the number of grouse chicks killed per male harrier was density dependent. In other words, the critical grouse densities, where the greatest percentage of the population would be removed per male harrier, appeared to be around 70 chicks per km². Below densities of 50 chicks per km² predation rates were relatively low. For a mean grouse brood size of six, 70 chicks per km² represents about 12 broods per km².

These conclusions are dependent on the findings from a different study in Glen Dye (Picozzi 1978). Further data are required at grouse densities above 70 chicks per km², ideally from Langholm, to see whether the relationship really levels off at this density. It is possible, for example, that habitat differences between study areas may influence the vulnerability of grouse chicks to harriers, so that harriers in different areas with the same density of grouse may take chicks at differing rates. Although the paucity of data at high grouse chick densities prevents us from assessing precisely at what densities the relationship levels off, the steepest part of the curve is represented by the four years at Langholm. Clearly, the relationship must level out at some stage, supporting the assertion that the curve is sigmoidal.

The relationship between harrier predation rates and grouse chicks was slightly different to that described by Redpath (1991) using earlier data from other areas. However, the two relationships pertain to different aspects of harrier predation on grouse and are thus not directly comparable. The earlier work focused on the percentage of grouse in the diet, whereas the present study used the measure of delivery rates of grouse. From the viewpoint of how many grouse chicks are removed from a grouse moor, the rate at which grouse chicks are brought to harrier nests is a more useful measure.

In addition to grouse chick density, one further important factor influenced the rate at which harriers (and particularly female harriers) took grouse chicks, namely breeding status. Both male and female harriers in bigamous relationships provisioned grouse chicks to their nests at a greater rate than monogamous birds. There were no clear differences in nest location between the two groups, and the pattern appeared to have been caused by the selection of larger prey by harriers involved in bigamous relationships. In this way, the harriers partly compensated for reduced overall provisioning rates at these nests. Lastly, females took grouse chicks at a greater rate when they had more chicks to feed.

In summary, available provisioning data indicated that predation by individual harriers on grouse chicks was likely to be highest at densities in the region of 70 chicks per km², especially where bigamy was prevalent. Clearly, overall levels of predation would also depend on the density of breeding harriers, a factor which seemed to be primarily influenced by the availability of small prey (Chapter 3). It would thus appear that Langholm moor, during the course of this study, provided conditions where we might have expected high levels of grouse chick predation. Small prey were abundant and attracted large numbers of harriers, many of which were bigamous, and grouse chick densities varied from 47 to 65 per km².

Grouse were an important component of harrier diet in the uplands overwinter, although the proportion of pellets in which they occurred varied substantially between areas. We found no statistically significant relationship between grouse abundance in the area around the roost and the proportion of grouse in the diet, presumably because other prey were locally more important in some areas. Small mammals were a substantial component of the winter pellets in some areas. If this pattern continued into early spring, it may explain why harrier breeding densities were influenced by the abundance of small mammals (Chapter 3). During summer, nest watches suggested that small mammals were relatively unimportant in the diet, possibly because of the wider availability of passerines and grouse chicks.

The proportion of peregrine pellets containing gamebirds varied according to time of year. Gamebirds most commonly occurred in pellets collected during winter, and least commonly in summer when pigeons and passerines occurred more frequently. There was considerable variation in the proportion of pellets containing gamebirds at any one abundance level of red grouse. Part of this variation may have been due to the fact that we were unable to distinguish different gamebird species in pellets, so, although we rarely found remains of other gamebird species in summer, some peregrines may have taken more pheasants near farmland or ptarmigan in the Highlands. Also, grouse abundance was estimated using the habitat within a 2 km radius of the eyrie. While Weir (1978) suggested that most grouse caught were from within this radius, peregrines travel greater distances to hunt (Ratcliffe 1993) so some prey may be captured further afield.

Caution is required when interpreting, as functional responses, the relationships between grouse density and the proportion of prey remains or pellets containing grouse. There are three main reasons for this.

- We have to assume that pellets are produced at similar rates across areas.
- Peregrines are likely to take different numbers of prey depending on what is available to them. Whereas a pair of peregrines with three chicks may have a fairly fixed biomass requirement for its brood, the number of individual prey items necessary to fill that requirement depends on the size of the prey. For this reason, a measure of grouse as a percentage of biomass is likely to be a more accurate reflection of the number of grouse taken.
- As data were drawn from different areas, the shape of the functional response curve may differ between areas because of some unmeasured area effects. Ideally, the effects of area could be controlled for by sampling the same eyries over a number of years in which prey densities varied. Such a study was not possible during the current project.

The sampled eyries ranged from the north of England to the central Highlands. There was a tendency for prey remains and pellets collected further north to contain a greater proportion of gamebirds, and this trend was statistically significant for prey remains. In summer, pigeons were numerically the most important prey, occurring in 67% of the pellets and forming 48% of all prey remains at eyries. This pattern of an increase in the proportion of grouse among the prey remains of peregrines in the north has been found previously (see Ratcliffe 1993), and probably reflects a decline in the abundance of pigeons with latitude, as discussed in Chapter 3. Our data from prey remains suggested that, in terms of both numbers and biomass, the proportion of grouse as prey levelled off at 20–40% at grouse densities above 20 per km². Total biomass requirements varied with peregrine brood size, but as breeding success did not appear to vary with grouse density (Chapter 3), the percentage of grouse in the diet by biomass is a better reflection of the total number of grouse removed.

The proportion of grouse in the pellets collected in summer also increased with grouse density, but levelled off at grouse densities over 20 per km². Extrapolating to single eyries, this relationship suggests that a pair of peregrines had its greatest impact at local grouse densities of below 10 pairs per km². Above this density, the proportion of available grouse taken was likely to decline. During winter, we collected no pellets from the Highlands, although other data from this region suggested that grouse were an important component in the diet. Thus, Weir (1978) showed that peregrines in Speyside overwinter fed largely on grouse, with red grouse and ptarmigan forming more than 80% of the diet by weight. The relationship between grouse density and the proportion of pellets containing gamebirds again suggests that the proportion of grouse as prey would be highest at local grouse densities around eyries of below 20 birds per km².

Overall, the data on peregrine diet suggested that the greatest proportion of grouse were removed at grouse densities below 20 birds per km². However, as stated earlier, peregrines may respond differently to changes in grouse density in different areas, and these relationships should be tested within areas over a range of grouse densities. From the data presented in this Chapter, we could not say whether raptors had a significant impact on grouse populations, but the relationships implied that a relatively greater proportion of the grouse were killed per harrier and per peregrine at low grouse densities.

Chapter 6

Female hen harrier quartering heather moorland

6. Estimates of grouse losses to raptors

- Estimates of the total number of grouse chicks removed by harriers at Langholm during each breeding season (April–August) ranged from 358 in 1993 to 1176 in 1994.
- Grouse chick losses to male harriers were estimated to be highest in the period from hatch to when the harrier chicks were four weeks old. Grouse chick losses to female harriers were highest from when the harrier chicks were four weeks old up to dispersal.
- Estimates of the total number of adult grouse removed by peregrines during each breeding season (April–August) ranged from 38 in 1992 to 174 in 1996.

INTRODUCTION

In previous Chapters, we discussed variation in the numbers, breeding success and diet of harriers and peregrines. In this Chapter, we use the diet and provisioning data from Langholm to estimate how many grouse these raptors removed from the population during a breeding season. For present purposes we are interested in the number of grouse estimated to have been taken by harriers and peregrines between the spring (start of April) and summer (middle of July) grouse counts, so that we can compare the numbers removed by these raptors to the total losses measured from grouse counts. In Chapter 8 we compare these estimates with grouse mortality rates and consider the impact of these losses on the grouse population.

Each calculation of grouse losses to raptors requires a number of assumptions and these, together with the tests of the assumptions (where possible), are stated explicitly in Appendix 3. Where possible we have used conservative estimates in our assumptions to give minimum figures for the numbers taken.

HARRIER PREDATION ON GROUSE DURING BREEDING SEASON

Estimates from Langholm moor of the numbers of grouse chicks removed by harriers were obtained from data collected during observations at nests (Chapter 5), and from knowledge of the numbers of harriers present (Chapter 3). Because the only two pairs of breeding harriers on the moor failed early in 1992, we assumed that there was no predation by harriers on grouse chicks in that year. The harrier breeding season was split into four periods:
- incubation,
- early nestling period (hatching to four weeks of age – 28 days),

- late nestling period (five weeks of age to fledging – 14 days),
- post-fledging period (fledging to dispersal – 18 days).

For each of these periods, predation by male and female harriers was assessed separately. Rates for males provisioning two females were combined to give figures per male rather than per nest. Estimates during these four periods were of grouse chicks only, as they formed 97% of all grouse taken at this time of year in our study, and 100% of those recorded by Picozzi (1978).

Incubation

Grouse chicks hatched towards the end of May. The median hatch date in 1995 was 28 May (N=24 radio-tagged broods, inter-quartile range 25 May–2 June) and the median date in 1996 was 30 May (N=33 radio-tagged broods, inter-quartiles 25 May–2 June). Grouse hatch coincided closely with harrier hatch date (median dates: 1995=29 May, 1996=28 May), so grouse chicks became available as the harriers' food requirements increased. Harriers which hatched after 28 May would probably have taken some grouse chicks between this date and hatching, and before nest watches commenced. We collected data on provisioning to incubating females by a total of seven males during 1994–96 (Table 6.1). On average, males were watched for 20.2 ± 6.0 hours, and provisioned their females at a rate of 0.51 ± 0.06 items per hour. We used this figure for provisioning rate, together with known male diet from nest watches, to estimate the total number of grouse chicks taken during incubation (Appendix 3). This number taken by all harriers varied from ten chicks in 1995 to 55 chicks in 1994 (Table 6.2).

Table 6.1 Rate at which prey items (grouse chicks in the early nestling period) were brought to nests by male and female harriers at Langholm each year during four periods: incubation, early nestling, late nestling and post-fledging. For female status, M=monogamous, α=alpha female of bigamous male, β=beta female of bigamous male. Hours relates to total number of hours the nest was watched. Rates for bigamous males to alpha and beta females were combined. % grouse relates to the percentage grouse in the diet during the third and fourth weeks of the early nestling period

Year	Nest	Female status	Hours	Items per h incubation Male	Grouse per h Early nestling Male	Grouse per h Early nestling Female	% grouse Early nestling Male	% grouse Early nestling Female	Items per h Late nestling Male	Items per h Late nestling Female	Items per h Post-fledging Male	Items per h Post-fledging Female
1993	1	M	125		0.013	0.071	3.22	9.52	0.667	1.167		
	2	M	156		0.020	0.040		1.96	3.28	0.819	0.541	
	3	M	134		0.074	0.074		4.58	21.28	0.791	0.316	
	4	M	185		0.057	0.033		4.88	12.70	0.767	0.736	
1994	1	α	84		0.120	0.060	12.19	14.29	0.706	0.112		
	2	β	106				0.11		50.00		0.374	
	3	α	73		0.121	0.009	13.51					
	4	β	32				0.063		14.29		0.306	
	5	M	111		0.097	0.056	14.63	9.76	0.523	0.382	0.000	0.452
	6	α	104	0.84	0.062	0.105	6.45	41.03		0.126	0.503	0.330
	7	β	117			0.157		33.33				0.618
	8	M	30	0.40								
	9	M	5	0.57								
1995	1	α	110		0.148	0.069	13.33	18.18	0.401	0.200		0.666
	2	β	105			0.095		45.71		0.586		
	3	M	123	0.35	0.012	0.023	0.00	22.22	0.000	0.300		
	4	M	114	0.50	0.105	0.041	19.74	28.12	0.111	0.111		
	5	α	153	0.38	0.159	0.062	6.90	15.00	0.325	0.418	0.053	0.300
	6	β	147			0.133		37.04		0.636		1.222
1996	1	α	158		0.040	0.000	24.39		0.263			
	2	M	147		0.078	0.039	9.76	15.09	0.164	0.764		
	3	α	133		0.064	0.031	6.12	37.50	0.573	0.227		
	4	β	114			0.144		33.33		0.375		
	5	M	102		0.012	0.024	1.90	13.79	0.683	0.260		
	6	α	6	0.56								
	7	β	4									

Early nestling period

During the first four weeks of nest watches, the rate that grouse chicks were brought to nests was determined from observations at nests (Table 6.2). These figures were then multiplied by the amount of time available in order to assess the total number of grouse removed (Appendix 3). Estimates of the total number of grouse chicks taken by all harriers during this period varied from 160 chicks in 1993 to 554 chicks in 1994 (Table 6.2).

Late nestling period

Harrier chicks first flew at about 35 days old, although they stayed close to the nest for approximately one further week. As prey identification became more difficult at this stage, the provisioning rate of grouse in this period was not used to estimate the numbers of grouse chicks removed. Instead, the total number of prey items brought to nests per hour was combined with the percentage of grouse in the diet during previous weeks (Appendix 3). Estimates of the total number of grouse chicks taken by all harriers during this period varied from 84 chicks in 1993 to 229 chicks in 1994 (Table 6.2).

Post-fledging period

To measure dispersal date, eight territories were watched in 1994 and 1995. These territories were visited every two or three days after fledging and watched for up to three hours at a time from vantage points until chicks were no longer seen. If no chicks were seen on one visit, territories were visited at least once more to check that the chicks had left. Dispersal date was taken as the day after the chicks were last observed. For the eight territories, the median number of days from hatching to dispersal was estimated to be 60 (range 58–64 days). Studies of harriers in North America have indicated between 45 and 66 days from hatch to dispersal (Beske 1982; Bildstein 1992). So, for the purposes of this publication, we consider that predation on grouse chicks continued for 18 days after the late nestling period.

Provisioning rates were measured during this post-fledging period by watching six territories from a distance. Three nests were watched in 1994 (mean time 11.9±3.8 h) and three in 1995 (mean time 10.0±0.4 h). Observations were limited to nests where the topography allowed us to ensure that all food passes were seen. In 1993 and 1996, we collected no provisioning data in this period, so we used an average provisioning rate from 1994 and 1995. In each year, we assessed predation rates by multiplying the provisioning rate by the percentage of grouse in the diet, in weeks 3 and 4 (Appendix 3). Estimates of the total number of grouse chicks taken by all harriers during this period varied from 83 chicks in 1993 to 496 chicks in 1996 (Table 6.2).

Total number of grouse chicks removed
Combining the figures for the four periods gave assessments of the total numbers of grouse chicks taken by all harriers at Langholm from 1993 to 1996 (Table 6.2).

These estimates varied from 358 chicks (4.3 per 0.5 km²) in 1993 to 1176 chicks (14.2 per 0.5 km²) in 1994.

The confidence that we could place in these estimates was largely based on how many nests we watched, compared to how many were present. During the post-fledging period a measure of variation in provisioning was obtained only in 1994. In this year the mean and 95% confidence intervals for the periods from hatching to dispersal were 1121.2±296.9 (see Appendix 3). In other words, we could be 95% confident that the true levels of grouse chick loss lay within 26% of our estimate (range 824–1418 chicks). For the other three years, we could estimate confidence intervals only from hatching to fledging: 1993, 244±68; 1995, 729±240; 1996, 652±272. Over this period, we could be 95% confident that our estimates lay within 28% in 1993, 32% in 1995 and 42% in 1996 of the estimated means.

Losses of adult grouse from 1 April to 17 July
In the paragraphs above, the number of grouse removed by harriers was estimated for each breeding season. We were also interested in comparing the estimates of numbers removed with the number that disappeared between the two grouse counting periods in April and July (Chapter 8).

Table 6.2 Estimates of grouse chick losses to all male and female harriers at Langholm, from harrier incubation to dispersal (see Appendix 3 for details of calculations)

	1993	1994	1995	1996
Successful males	4	6	6	7
Successful females	4	9	8	12
Incubation				
Male totals	31.5	55.2	9.6	17.8
Early nestling period				
Male totals	68.9±25.2	252.0±35.3	267.1±83.2	149.9±58.8
Female totals	90.7±16.8	302.4±68.0	235.2±53.8	282.2±110.9
Total grouse (early nestling)	159.6±30.3	554.4±76.6	502.3±99.1	432.2±125.5
Late nestling period				
Male totals	23.5±4.2	102.1±6.3	30.2±13.8	30.9±10.2
Female totals	60.5±9.0	126.6±57.7	196.6±72.7	189.0±54.3
Total grouse (late nestling)	84.0±9.9	228.7±58.0	226.8±74.0	219.9±55.2
Post-fledging period				
Male totals	7.3	26.3±26.3	5.9	15.5
Female totals	75.5	311.8±114.2	384.4±295.9	480.8
Total grouse (post-fledging)	82.8	338.1±117.2	390.3	496.3
Total grouse chicks taken	357.9	1176.4	1129.0	1166.2
Grouse chicks taken per 0.5 km²	4.3	14.2	13.6	14.0

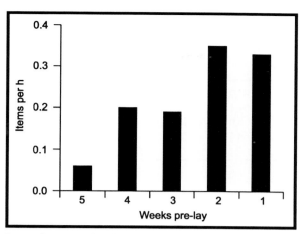

Figure 6.1 Rate of male harrier provisioning during the pre-lay period. Data given as mean per male±SE, in each of the five weeks leading up to egg laying

Any significant predation by harriers on adult grouse must have taken place in early April, before laying. Once female harriers started incubating, it was unlikely that they killed any adult grouse for six weeks, and once they started hunting to feed their chicks at Langholm adult grouse formed less than 0.2% of prey items. Males killed practically no adult grouse. The median date for initiation of egg laying in harriers was 27 April. We had no information on the prey captured by females in April, so we could not estimate the number of grouse removed by them. However, we knew that they were fed by their males before egg laying, and that all male food seen at this time of year was small (passerines and small mammals see Chapter 4). Males were seen to provision their females from 21 March, in this case 35 days before egg laying. The rate of provisioning increased up to laying (Figure 6.1), and differences between weeks were statistically significant (controlling for year: $F_{1,47}$=12.42, P<0.001).

Table 6.3 Summary of estimated losses of grouse chicks to harriers before and after 17 July, based on data in Table 6.2 and Appendix 3

	1993	1994	1995	1996
Before 17 July	257.2	917.4	931.3	804.6
Per 0.5 km²	3.1	11.0	11.2	9.7
After 17 July	100.7	259.0	197.7	361.6
Per 0.5 km²	1.2	3.1	2.4	4.4
Total	357.9	1176.4	1129.0	1166.2
Per 0.5 km²	4.3	14.2	13.6	14.0

Data from other studies have suggested that at least one week prior to laying, the females enter an 'egg laying lethargy' during which they do no hunting and their food requirements are met entirely by the males (Newton 1979; Simmons et al. 1986). Observed provisioning rates by males were high in the two weeks leading up to laying, suggesting that the males supplied most of the food in these two weeks. As male provisioning increased from the start of April, it was likely that, for most females, hunting declined from the start of April and stopped by the third week. Any significant predation by harriers on adult grouse would therefore have occurred in the first two weeks of April. Assuming females caught no prey in the two weeks prior to laying, and knowing lay dates for each female, we estimated the number of days in April available for hunting by the total population of females. In rank order, the years were: 1994 (183 harrier days), 1996 (169 harrier days), 1993 (105 harrier days), 1995 (91 harrier days) and 1992 (28 harrier days). If predation on grouse by female harriers was high at this time of year, we predicted that the level of grouse mortality in each year would reflect the rank order of these figures. This aspect is considered further in Chapter 7.

Losses of grouse chicks from 1 April to 17 July
Using the same method described above, we estimated the number of grouse chicks removed by the harrier population before the grouse counts occurred in mid-July. By 17 July some harrier broods had dispersed, but many were still being fed by their parents. For each of the four periods (incubation, early nestling, late nestling and post-fledging) in each year, we counted the total number of days that harriers were present before 17 July. These figures were multiplied by the relevant provisioning rate for each period and summed to give estimates of grouse chick losses to all harriers up to mid-July in each year (Appendix 3). Final estimates of chick losses indicated that by 17 July harriers had removed between 257 and 931 grouse chicks from the moor (Table 6.3). We earlier estimated that there was approximately 41.4 km² of heather moorland at Langholm (Chapter 2). Equivalent figures per 0.5 km² were between 3 and 11 chicks.

Table 6.4 The number of prey items collected and the percentage biomass consisting of grouse at Langholm peregrine eyries in different years

Eyrie	1992 Items	%	1993 Items	%	1994 Items	%	1995 Items	%	1996 Items	%	All years Items	%
St	23	0.0	14	14.0	47	0.0	28	0.0	11	0.0	123	1.8
Di	23	12.9	9	0.0	20	44.2	39	14.1	24	16.4	115	19.3
So	–	–	–	–	–	–	32	9.9	60	24.0	92	19.2
Lo	–	–	–	–	4	0.0	6	58.3	36	24.9	46	26.5
Ms	–	–	–	–	2	0.0	–	–	32	22.7	34	22.0

– No data

PEREGRINE PREDATION ON GROUSE DURING BREEDING SEASON

To assess summer predation rates by peregrines on grouse, we used a different approach to the one used for harriers, basing our estimates on peregrine dietary requirements and prey remains. We only considered predation by peregrines which were on territory in spring and summer. Non-territorial birds might have been present, but we had no information on how many or what they ate. Estimates were determined for three periods: incubation, nestling and post-fledging.

Biomass requirements

Over the five summers at Langholm, we collected 410 prey remains from the five eyries on the moor, of which 43 items were grouse. In terms of biomass, the relative importance of grouse varied between eyries at Langholm from 1.8% to 26.5% (Table 6.4). As there were small sample sizes at eyries in some years, we used data for eyries from all years combined. The biomass estimates of the prey were obtained from Table 8 in Ratcliffe (1993).

In order to calculate from biomass measures the total number of grouse removed, we first

Table 6.5 Summary of information gained from watches at three peregrine nests at Langholm

	Nest 1	Nest 2	Nest 3
Year	1995	1996	1996
Site	Di	Di	Lo
Hatch date	10 May	12 May	13 May
Dates watched	22 May–1June	23May–7June	17–30May
Nos of chicks	3	3	4
Hours watched	42.4	52.0	80.5
Nos of items	13	12	29
Nos of grouse	1	4	2
Items per h	0.307	0.231	0.360
Biomass (g)	2948	3625	6791
Biomass per h	69.5	69.7	84.4

considered the food requirements of a peregrine brood. This was estimated during observations at one peregrine nest in 1995 and at two nests in 1996, during the chick rearing period (Table 6.5). These watches at Langholm indicated an average of 1118±128 g of prey per day, equivalent to 47.0 kg over six weeks. On average, each chick required 222 g per day, or 9324 g over the six-week period, and each adult required 188 g per day or 7896 g over the six-week period (Appendix 3). An average grouse weight was taken as 637 g in spring and 607 g in summer to account for the fact that 10% of grouse found at peregrine eyries were juveniles.

Incubation

Although peregrines generally did not start laying until around 7 April, we took the start of the breeding season as 1 April, to coincide with grouse counts. The median hatch date at Langholm was 10 May (range 2 May–5 June), so, for the purposes of our calculations, incubation was taken as 40 days. As each adult required 188 g per day, we estimated that the total prey requirements during incubation were 7.52 kg. The percentage of grouse in the diet, by biomass, was then used to estimate how many grouse were consumed in this period by breeding peregrines at Langholm (Appendix 3). Estimates ranged from only ten grouse taken by all breeding peregrines in 1992 to 24 in 1994 and 1995 (Table 6.6).

Nestling period

The period from hatching to fledging was approximately 6 weeks (42 days). Over this period, we estimated the adult food requirements at 7.9 kg, and each chick's requirements at 9.3 kg of prey. Using these measures and the percentage of grouse in the diet at each eyrie, we estimated the number of grouse removed during this

Table 6.6. Estimated numbers of grouse killed by peregrines during their breeding season at Langholm 1992–96. Calculations are shown in Appendix 3

	1992	1993	1994	1995	1996
Number of peregrine pairs	3	3	6	6	5
Number of grouse killed					
Incubation	10.1	10.1	24.5	24.5	20.9
Nestling period	11.7	12.0	36.9	43.1	67.2
Post-fledging period	16.7	17.0	50.4	58.1	86.1
Total number taken	38.5	39.1	111.8	125.7	174.2
Numbers per 0.5 km^2	0.5	0.5	1.3	1.5	2.1
After 17 July	7.2	7.3	21.7	25.0	37.0
1 April to 17 July	31.3	31.8	90.1	100.7	137.2
Numbers per 0.5 km^2	0.4	0.4	1.1	1.2	1.6

period (Appendix 3). Estimates ranged from 12 grouse removed by all breeding peregrines in 1992 and 1993 to 67 grouse in 1996 (Table 6.6).

Post-fledging period

Ratcliffe (1993) estimated that peregrine chicks stayed on territory for at least two months after fledging. For the purpose of our calculations, we assumed a period of 60 days from fledging to dispersal. Food requirements of chicks would be expected to decline once the chicks had stopped growing and left the nest. So, over this period, we considered adult and chick food requirements to be the same (11.2 kg). Again, we used these measures to calculate the total number of grouse removed during this period (Appendix 3). Estimates varied from 17 grouse taken by all breeding peregrines in 1992 and 1993 to 86 grouse in 1996 (Table 6.6).

Failed breeders

In four of the five years some peregrines failed to breed successfully. In each year, failed breeders stayed on the moor throughout the summer. At one site (Rf), used unsuccessfully in two years, we were unable to collect sufficient remains for prey estimates. For this site we took an average value based on the diet of other Langholm peregrines. Failed breeders were assumed to have the same biomass requirements throughout the period when the other peregrines were breeding.

Total numbers of grouse removed by peregrines

In each year, we could combine the estimates of grouse losses at different stages to give a total figure for the number of grouse taken by the peregrine population during their breeding season (Table 6.6). These losses ranged from 38 grouse in 1992 to 174 grouse in 1996. We earlier estimated that there was approximately 41.4 km^2 of heather moorland at Langholm (Chapter 2). Equivalent figures per 0.5 km^2 of heather moorland were therefore 0.5 and 2.0. These numbers were small compared to the total number of grouse chicks removed by harriers.

Numbers of grouse removed from 1 April to 17 July

Grouse counts were conducted on 1 April and 17 July. To calculate losses over this period, we merely excluded losses that occurred from 17 July to dispersal (Appendix 3). The estimates of the total number of grouse removed by all peregrines at Langholm between the counts varied from 31 grouse (0.4 per 0.5 km^2) in 1992 to 137 grouse (1.6 per 0.5 km^2) in 1996 (Table 6.6).

PREDATION IN WINTER

There were two problems in estimating the numbers of grouse removed by raptors in the winter. First, it was difficult to estimate accurately the number of individual raptors hunting the moor. Second, dietary information was based on pellet information only. While pellets were useful in a comparative study of diet within and between areas (Chapter 5), they were less useful in assessing predation rates. It was not possible to say from pellets how many individual grouse had been eaten. The majority of peregrine pellets contained more than one prey type, suggesting that the pellets were composed of a number of prey items eaten in previous days. The presence of grouse feathers in a pellet indicated that the peregrine had eaten grouse, but we could not say when or how many. Also, we would need to know for wild peregrines the rate of pellet ejection and the length of time an adult grouse would keep a peregrine in food, on neither of which points had we good information. For these reasons we did not use pellet information to estimate the total number of grouse killed by raptors in winter, relying instead on information from finds of kills and radio-tracking (Chapter 7).

DISCUSSION

In this Chapter we have used information on harrier and peregrine diet to estimate the number of grouse removed during spring and summer at Langholm. The accuracy of these estimates depends on the number and validity of the assumptions employed in the calculations. Where possible, we have erred on the side of caution, so that our estimates are likely to represent minimum values.

Two inherent assumptions in all the calculations were that our observations gave a true picture of what was happening at that nest, and that the nests watched were representative of all those on the moor. The confidence we can place in the estimates partly depends on how long each nest was watched and how many of the available nests were monitored. For harriers, we spent on average between 12% (1994) and 21% (1996) of all available time in the first six weeks at each nest, and between 42% (1996) and 100% (1993) of nests were watched in any one year. Nests were observed in the same part of the moor in each year, so the findings should have been comparable between years. Moreover, pellet analysis suggested that the prey composition was similar between observed nests and the unobserved ones. The ratio of monogamous to bigamous harriers watched was not always equal to the ratio of available birds (Appendix 3). As bigamous harriers took more grouse than monogamous ones, this discrepancy could have led to a slight overestimate of the number of grouse chicks killed in 1994 and an underestimate in 1996.

The pattern of predation by harriers on grouse chicks indicated that predation by males was highest in weeks 1–4, when the overall provisioning rates and the proportions of

grouse in their diets were high. Predation by females was estimated to be highest after their chicks fledged, when their provisioning rates appeared to peak. Our data on provisioning for this period were based only on 60 hours, and we were unable to estimate confidence intervals for this period in three of the four years. We know of no other studies which examined provisioning rates in detail after fledging, so had no other information for comparison.

Picozzi (1978) estimated that a pair of harriers removed approximately 255 grouse chicks before the young harriers dispersed. Equivalent figures for our study varied between 89 chicks per nest in 1993 and 141 chicks per nest in 1995. Picozzi's studies were conducted at high grouse density (41 pairs per km²), and provisioning rates of grouse chicks to harrier nests were higher. Picozzi went on to estimate that all harriers removed 7.4% of the grouse population from the moor. Estimates of the proportion of the grouse population removed by raptors at Langholm were higher, as discussed in Chapter 8.

Our estimates of the number of grouse killed by peregrines came from dietary requirements and prey remains, and suggested that the number killed by the Langholm peregrines in any one year ranged from 38 in 1992 to 174 in 1996. Weir (1978) stated that peregrine chicks required up to 300 g of prey per day, depending on their age, whereas an adult required 175 g. Ratcliffe (1993) estimated that an adult peregrine required approximately 159 g of prey per day. These figures suggest that our estimates of 222 g per day for a chick and 188 g per day for the adults were of the right order. The main assumption was that biomass from prey remains was a true representation of eaten prey, although comparisons from prey remains and nest watches suggested that, if anything, grouse biomass from remains may have slightly underestimated the real value.

Weir (1978) estimated that a pair of peregrines with four young could remove during the breeding season roughly 110 red grouse and ptarmigan from a territory in the Highlands. Equivalent figures, based on similar biomass calculations, for a successful pair at Langholm varied from 3 to 59 grouse, depending on the location of the eyrie. Again, these estimates were considerably lower than in Weir's study, because grouse were a more important prey in his area, forming 40% by weight.

Our estimates suggested that at Langholm many more grouse were killed by the harrier population than by the peregrine population, although most harrier predation was on chicks, and most peregrine predation on adults. Female harriers may have removed adult grouse in early April before they started forming eggs. The extent of this predation was unknown, because we had no data on female prey at this time, although any predation by harriers in April should have been influenced by differences in the number of breeding birds and laying date between years, which in turn should have been reflected in grouse mortality patterns (Chapter 8).

The total number of grouse that were estimated to have been removed by harriers and peregrines at Langholm varied between years according to:
• the number of raptors present,
• the number of young they raised, and
• their provisioning rate.

Grouse were brought to harrier nests at a faster rate where grouse were most abundant (Chapter 5), so in general the number of grouse removed in spring and summer increased with grouse density and with the number of successfully breeding raptors. Estimates of the number of grouse removed per 0.5 km² were based on the number of hectare squares where heather formed over 30% of the cover (Chapter 2). This may have been a slight underestimate of the ground occupied by grouse, because some birds occurred at low density on areas where heather cover was less than 30%. The data presented above gave estimates of the number of grouse removed by raptors, but they did not tell us whether these losses were important in limiting the grouse population. This aspect is further explored in Chapter 8.

Chapter 7

Male red grouse in winter snow

7. Patterns of predation

- The grouse population at Langholm did not increase or decrease significantly during the five years of study.
- Grouse counts at Langholm in October and April demonstrated that winter losses averaged 33%. Winter losses were density dependent, with a higher proportion of grouse lost from areas where densities were high in October than from areas where densities were low.
- Carcase searching showed that raptors were the proximate cause of 70% of the observed winter mortality of grouse and that they killed the equivalent of 30% of the grouse counted in October. The difference between winter losses and winter mortality suggested that the counting sites consistently gained grouse through immigration.
- Grouse counts at Langholm in April and July demonstrated that summer losses of adult grouse averaged 30%. Summer losses of adult grouse were density dependent.
- Annual survival of radio-tagged grouse at Langholm during 1994–95 and 1995–96 was estimated at 30%. This figure was similar to those found in other studies of red grouse.
- Estimates of the cause and rate of winter mortality determined by radio-tagging during 1994–95 and 1995–96 were similar to those obtained by counts and carcase searching.
- Estimates of summer mortality rates of adult grouse determined by radio-tagging during 1995 and 1996 were similar to the observed summer losses between the April and July counts. More than 90% of the early summer mortality of radio-tagged adult grouse was due to raptor predation.
- Estimates of grouse chick losses derived from brood counts during 1995 and 1996 suggest that 45% of chicks disappeared between chick hatch at the end of May and grouse counts at the end of July. Summer losses of grouse chicks were not density dependent.

INTRODUCTION

Red grouse fall prey to a range of avian and mammalian predators. There has been considerable debate as to whether predation can limit red grouse populations, reflecting a wider controversy regarding the role of vertebrate predators in limiting prey numbers (reviewed by Crawley 1992; Newton 1993; Côté & Sutherland 1997). There have been two previous studies of predation on red grouse. The first, during the late 1950s, on high-density grouse populations with few predators, concluded that predation had little impact on either breeding densities or breeding success (Jenkins *et al.* 1963, 1964). More recently, Hudson (1990, 1992), working on low-density grouse populations with many predators, concluded that predation reduced both breeding densities and breeding success and prevented low-density grouse populations from increasing.

Our aim in the current study was to determine whether predation limited red grouse populations at Langholm. As a first step, we present information on the basic patterns of predation observed. We use these data in subsequent Chapters to investigate to what extent predation is additive to other mortality and to determine whether it reduces the numbers of grouse available for shooting in autumn and breeding in spring (Chapter 8). We also examine the effect of habitat on grouse demography (Chapter 9). Here, however, we first describe how predation rates vary temporally and spatially within the grouse population at Langholm and examine whether predation is density dependent. We assess the importance of raptor predation in relation to other causes of mortality and examine both the timing of predation and whether predators kill certain age-sex classes of grouse preferentially. On Langholm moor, foxes and crows were controlled during the study, but raptors were not.

Our data come from three main sources.
- We counted grouse with pointing dogs on 12 0.5 km² sites at Langholm during April,

Table 7.1 April, July and October grouse densities at Langholm during 1992–96. Data from counts with dogs. Values are mean±SE for 12 0.5 km² counting areas

Year	1992	1993	1994	1995	1996
April	–	14.4±2.1	17.8±2.3	15.3±1.7	13.6±1.8
July	34.1±6.3	32.8±4.3	36.6±5.9	31.8±4.5	27.8±3.6
Oct	24.8±3.3	23.3±3.0	22.9±3.2	20.7±2.8	26.8±2.4

July and October in each year during 1992–96. On each of the counting sites, we conducted systematic searches for grouse carcases in each month from October to March. Grouse carcases were recovered and, where possible, the cause of death was determined from field signs.

- We captured and radio-tagged grouse in October 1994, September 1995 and March 1996, and monitored their survival during October 1994 to September 1996. Radio-tagging provided an independent measure of the rates and causes of mortality.
- We obtained estimates of grouse brood sizes at hatch, during the first week in June and again during the third week in July, through radio-tagging hens and by searching for broods with pointing dogs.

Details of the methods used are given in Chapter 2.

PATTERNS OF ADULT MORTALITY: GROUSE COUNTS AND CARCASE SEARCHING

Grouse density

Overall, the grouse population at Langholm remained relatively stable over the study period with no significant trends between years in April, July or October densities (Table 7.1, ANCOVA removing site effects: April $F_{2,35}$=1.47, P=0.23; July $F_{2,47}$=1.77, P=0.19; October $F_{2,47}$=0.05, P=0.82). However, the local variation in grouse density within the moor was considerable, as indicated by the changes on different 0.5 km² study sites (Figure 7.1). Changes in April, July and October grouse densities between years showed few consistent patterns; in most pairs of years some sites showed an increase in density whilst others showed a decrease.

Rates of winter mortality

Our first approach to quantify the rates of winter mortality was to use the October and April grouse counts in conjunction with searches for grouse carcases on each of the counting sites during each winter month. These data gave us the following demographic variables:

- *winter loss* – the difference between October and April grouse counts on each site;
- *winter kills* – the number of grouse carcases found on each site which were judged to have died between 1 October and 31 March;
- *unexplained change* – the difference between winter loss and winter kills on each site assumed to represent net losses or gains through movement of grouse.

Taking the values from the 12 counting sites, there were no significant changes in any of these three demographic variables over the four winters (Table 7.2, ANCOVA removing site effects: winter loss $F_{2,35}$=1.09, P=0.30; winter kills $F_{2,35}$=0.12, P=0.73; unexplained change $F_{2,35}$=0.75, P=0.39). In other words, there was no significant change over the four winters of the study in either the extent of the overwinter reduction in grouse numbers, the numbers of grouse found dead, or the extent of unexplained changes in grouse numbers attributed to movement. In each winter, the average losses were less than the average number of grouse found dead on the counting sites, suggesting that there was a net influx of grouse overwinter. These figures can be put into perspective by expressing them as a percentage of the grouse densities in October. Thus, April grouse numbers were on average 33% lower than numbers the previous October, the number of grouse found dead on each site represented on average 43% of the number of grouse counted on each site in October, and the unexplained changes in grouse numbers, in this case gains assumed to be through immigration, averaged 10% of the numbers counted in the previous October (Table 7.2).

These analyses concentrated on examining variation between years in average winter loss, winter kills and unexplained changes in grouse density over the moor as a whole (as reflected in the 12 counting sites). There were, however, significant area differences in winter kills and unexplained change in grouse density within each winter of the

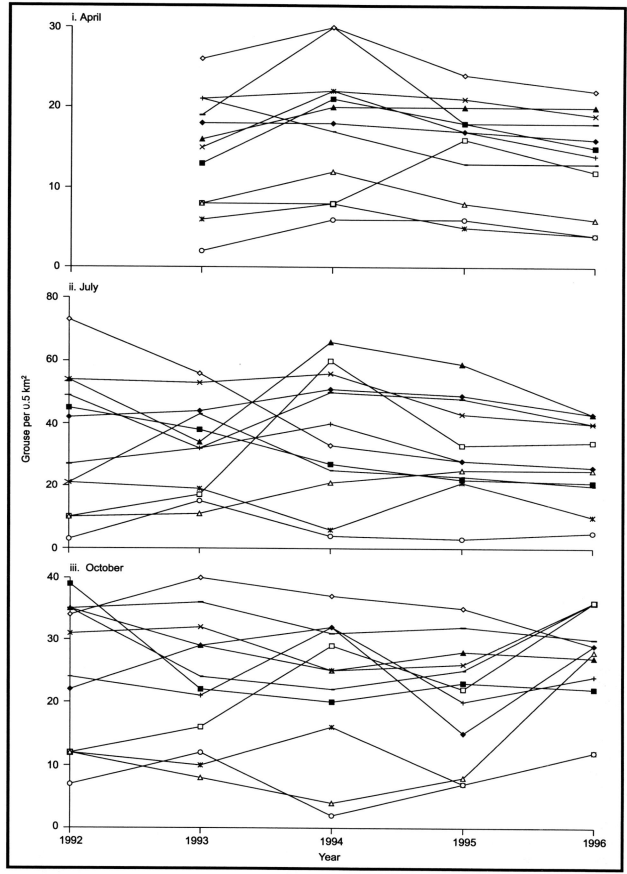

Figure 7.1 Grouse densities at Langholm in the years 1992–96 on each of the 0.5 km² counting sites in (i) April; (ii) July; and (iii) October. Successive counts on the same sites are joined by lines

Table 7.2 October and April grouse density and winter loss, kills and unexplained change at Langholm. Data from grouse counts and carcase searches. Values are mean±SE of 12 0.5 km² counting areas. All percentages relate to October grouse densities

Winter	1992–93	1993–94	1994–95	1995–96
October grouse	24.8±3.3	23.3±3.0	22.9±3.2	20.7±2.8
April grouse	14.4±2.1	17.8±2.3	15.3±1.7	13.6±1.8
Winter loss (%)	10.4±2.2 (41.9)	5.4±1.4 (23.2)	7.7±2.0 (33.6)	7.1±1.4 (34.3)
Winter kills (%)	10.8±1.7 (43.5)	9.2±2.2 (39.5)	9.2±1.7 (40.2)	10.3±2.4 (49.8)
Unexplained change (%)	0.4±2.3 (1.6)	3.8±2.0 (16.3)	1.5±1.7 (6.6)	3.2±1.7 (15.5)

study (ANCOVA removing year effect: winter kills $F_{2,35}=14.33$, $P<0.001$; unexplained change $F_{2,35}=2.64$, $P=0.01$). Within-winter area differences in winter loss were not quite statistically significant (ANCOVA removing year effect: $F_{2,35}=1.71$, $P=0.11$). These differences in findings between counting sites were not surprising because sites were chosen to be representative of the six grouse shooting beats, and in practice grouse densities varied by an order of magnitude between them (Figure 7.1).

Causes of winter mortality

Systematic searches for corpses combined with *ad hoc* discoveries during other fieldwork resulted in the recovery of 474 grouse carcases from the 12 counting sites over the four winters 1992–96. Where possible, we determined the cause of death of each bird and classified grouse as having been killed by raptors, killed by mammals, or as having died from other causes. We were confident in our ability to distinguish raptor kills from mammal kills but could not reliably distinguish between predation by different species of raptors or mammals (Thirgood *et al.* 1997, Chapter 2).

Raptor predation was the most important proximate cause of mortality in each winter (Table 7.3). Raptors killed on average 6.8 grouse on each 0.5 km² counting site in each winter, corresponding on average to 70% of the grouse found dead overwinter and to 30% of the grouse counted on those sites in October. There was no significant change between the four winters of the

study in either the numbers of grouse killed overwinter by raptors or the ratio of raptor kills to all winter mortality (ANCOVA removing site effect: raptor kills $F_{2,35}=1.31$, $P=0.26$; ratio of raptor kills to all winter mortality $F_{2,35}=2.62$, $P=0.12$). It should be stressed, however, that foxes were subject to control by gamekeepers, and this may have reduced the impact of foxes on the grouse population.

Were winter losses density dependent?

To evaluate the effects of predation on a population, it is necessary to understand how predation rates vary in relation to prey density. The concept of density dependence is deceptively simple, but demonstrating density dependence in real populations is not straightforward. In our case, an intuitive approach would be to examine how winter losses on each counting site varied in relation to October grouse density. There were, however, several problems in this approach. First, we were interested in changes in the rate of winter loss, not in the numbers of birds disappearing. Rates could be expressed as percentages, but comparing percentage loss between different densities could be misleading, because predation events at low density could have large effects on rates. More fundamentally, such analyses would violate assumptions of statistical independence because both dependent and independent variables included October density.

A more rigorous approach in testing for density dependence in overwinter loss is to compare the numbers of grouse on each counting site in October with the numbers of grouse on each site in April, ie before and after any cause of loss. A standard test for

Table 7.3 October grouse densities and causes of winter mortality at Langholm. Data from grouse counts and carcase searches. Values are mean±SE of 12 0.5 km² counting areas. All percentages relate to October grouse densities

Winter	1992–93	1993–94	1994–95	1995–96
October grouse	24.8±3.3	23.3±3.0	22.9±3.2	20.7±2.8
Raptor kills (%)	6.4±1.1 (25.8)	6.6±1.7 (28.3)	6.5±1.4 (28.4)	7.9±2.3 (38.2)
Mammal kills (%)	3.2±0.6 (12.9)	1.9±0.5 (8.2)	2.1±0.4 (9.2)	1.7±0.5 (8.2)
Other deaths (%)	1.2±0.4 (4.8)	0.7±0.2 (3.0)	0.6±0.3 (2.6)	0.7±0.3 (3.4)

7. Patterns of predation

density dependence uses the slope in the regression of log April density on log October density. The null hypothesis is rejected when the slope is significantly less than one, using Student's t-test. Applying this test to our grouse counts gave the linear regression of log April density on the previous log October density (Figure 7.2) as:

Equation 7.1
ln April density = 0.446 + 0.720 ln October density

The standard error on the estimated slope was 0.083, giving a t-ratio for unit slope as $t_{46} = -3.40$, P<0.01. This analysis thus suggested strong evidence for density dependence. However, the plot shown in Figure 7.2 included both within- and between-site effects. We also needed to know which of these was important:

- was it that areas with high grouse densities consistently lost a high proportion of grouse (a between-site effect), or
- did each area show a tendency to lose a higher proportion of grouse in years when densities were high (a within-site effect)?

When we augmented the above analysis by adding an individual site effect, we found that the estimated slope was 0.048

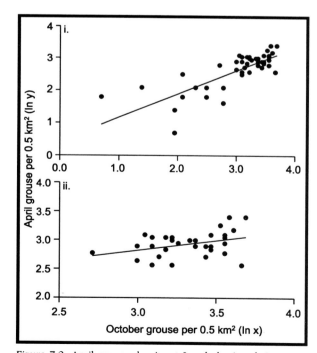

Figure 7.2 April grouse density at Langholm in relation to the previous October grouse density over the years 1992–96 on (i) each of the 0.5 km² counting sites, and (ii) the restricted set of 0.5 km² counting sites excluding sites 5, 6, 11 and 12. Data are ln-transformed

(SE=0.129), giving a t-ratio for unit slope as $t_{46} = -7.38$, P<0.001, which appeared to provide even stronger evidence of density dependence. However, there was also evidence for differences between sites ($F_{3,43} = 4.96$, P<0.001). The t-ratios for the site effects measured relative to site 1 revealed that four sites had relatively high overwinter losses: site 5, t=−5.15; site 6, t=−5.27; site 11, t=−2.55; site 12, t=−2.86. If we dropped the site effect and added a year effect, then the estimated slope was 0.728 (SE=0.091), with a t-ratio for unit slope as $t_{46} = -3.36$, P<0.01. Differences between years were not statistically significant ($F_{3,43} = 1.90$, P=0.14), although there was a suggestion of lower overwinter loss in 1993–94.

From the preceding analysis, there seemed to be a reasonable case for omitting sites 5, 6, 11 and 12 from the analysis of density dependence. The reasons are as follows.

- We were interested in predicting a likely increase in density, so what was happening at higher October densities was more relevant than responses at low densities.
- All the very low October counts occurred at these sites. Such counts were likely to be sensitive to sampling errors and movements of grouse.
- Sites 5 and 6 were unusual in having very low heather cover and sites 11 and 12 were relatively isolated at 5 km west of the main moorland block (Figure 2.8).

We repeated this analysis omitting sites 5, 6, 11 and 12, which gave the linear regression of log April density on the previous log October density (Figure 7.2) as:

Equation 7.2
ln April density = 1.791 + 0.343 ln October density

The standard error on the estimated slope was 0.154, giving a t-ratio for unit slope as $t_{30} = -4.26$, P<0.001. This analysis again suggested strong evidence for density dependence. However, the plot in Figure 7.2 also included both within- and between-site effects. Adding a year effect to the model, the estimated slope was 0.325 (SE=0.155), giving a t-ratio for unit slope as $t_{27} = -4.35$, P<0.001. The overall analysis therefore largely reflected the pattern of density dependence between sites.

Differences between years were not statistically significant ($F_{3,27}$=2.52, P=0.08). When we dropped the year effect and added a site effect, then the estimated slope was 0.010 (SE=0.185), giving a t-ratio for unit slope as t_{22}=−5.35, P<0.001. Differences between sites were not statistically significant ($F_{7,23}$=1.78, P=0.4). The almost zero slope, which seemed to imply even stronger density dependence, may reflect the small range of densities over the four years at each site. Although the slope was close to zero, we could not claim that it was less than the slope for spatial density dependence across sites within years. In other words, the data were consistent with a single pattern of density dependence in winter loss which applied across sites within years and across years within sites.

Lack of statistical independence and pseudoreplication

The above analysis treated all the observations as statistically independent. However, the same sites were used across years and different sites were likely to be affected in similar ways in each year. Tests for density dependence which combine sites across years or years across sites need to allow for the possibility of lack of statistical independence. Suppose that we tested for spatial density dependence across sites within a year. For a given year j, a plausible model for analysis relates April and October densities by:

Equation 7.3
$\ln$ April density$_i$ = a$_j$ + b $\ln$ October density + s$_i$ + Z$_{ij}$

where the intercept in the density-dependent relationship (a$_j$) was allowed to vary between years. The term s$_i$ represented a random effect for the ith site, and its presence in the model correlated the observations on the same site in different years. The term Z$_{ij}$ was another random effect for the variation remaining after allowing for persistent site effects which were assumed to be independent across sites and years. The total variance of the random component was equal to V_T=V_s+V_Z.

The above model could be fitted using the method of residual maximum likelihood to provide the following estimates of the slope coefficient and the variance components:

b=0.088 (SE=0.158), V_s=0.014 (SE=0.011), V_z=0.025 (SE=0.008). The estimated variance component for sites accounted for 35% of the total, but its addition to the model was not statistically significant. Allowing for correlation between observations on the same site hardly affected the standard error of the estimated slope coefficient, and the t-ratio for unit slope was t_{46}=−5.77, P<0.001.

We did a similar analysis to test for temporal density dependence across years within sites by allowing the intercept to vary across sites and including a random year effect. The slope coefficient and variance estimates were b=−0.087 (SE=0.169), V_t=0.012, V_z=0.024. The estimated variance component for years accounted for about 30% of the total but its addition to the model was not statistically significant. The test for unit slope emerged as highly statistically significant with t_{46}=−6.43, P<0.001.

The above findings are essentially the same as those from the simpler analyses which ignored problems of pseudoreplication. Our conclusion of spatial and temporal density dependence in winter loss remains unchanged.

Were winter density-dependent losses due to raptor predation?

The preceding analysis suggested that winter losses at Langholm were density dependent, with a higher proportion of grouse lost overwinter with increasing grouse density. To what extent was this density dependence driven by raptor predation? Linear regression analysis demonstrated that both the number of raptor kills and the number of non-raptor kills found in winter on the counting sites increased significantly with October grouse density (raptor kills $F_{1,46}$=38.55, P<0.001; non-raptor kills $F_{1,46}$=8.54, P=0.005). However, the ratio of raptor kills/non-raptor kills also increased significantly with October grouse density ($F_{1,46}$=6.97, P=0.01), suggesting that raptor predation could have been the proximate cause of much of the observed density dependence in overwinter loss.

Rates of summer loss of adult grouse

Because we did not conduct systematic carcase searches on our counting sites

Table 7.4 April and July adult grouse density and summer loss at Langholm. Data from grouse counts. Values are mean±SE of 12 0.5 km² counting areas. All percentages relate to April grouse densities

Year	1992–93	1993–94	1994–95	1995–96
April grouse	14.4±2.1	17.8±2.3	15.3±1.7	13.6±1.8
July grouse	12.3±1.4	11.7±1.6	9.4±1.0	9.0±1.2
Summer loss (%)	2.2±1.2 (15.3)	6.2±1.6 (34.8)	5.8±1.2 (37.9)	4.6±1.0 (33.8)

throughout the summer, we are restricted to using counts of living grouse on these sites to investigate the summer loss of adult grouse rather than summer mortality *per se*. We define *summer loss* as the difference between the number of adult grouse counted in the beginning of April and the number counted at the end of July on each counting site. This definition makes no assumptions regarding the cause of loss and may thus include movement as well as mortality. We use July counts in preference to October counts because it is possible to distinguish at several metres distance (typical flushing distance on counts) between old and young grouse in July but not in October.

The average values for summer loss observed at Langholm during 1993–96 are shown in Table 7.4. Levels of summer loss tended to be lower in 1993 than in the

following years, but the difference was not statistically significant (ANCOVA removing site effect: $F_{2,35}$=0.53, P=0.67). These figures for summer loss can be put into context by expressing them as a percentage of the grouse population counted in April. Thus, in the four years 1993–96, an average of 30% of the adult grouse population disappeared from each counting site between early April and late July. However, there were significant between-site differences in the extent of summer loss within each year of the study (ANCOVA removing year effect: $F_{2,35}$=3.10, P=0.006).

Were summer losses of adult grouse density dependent?

We adopted a similar approach in testing for density dependence in summer loss of adult grouse as we did for winter loss. We compared the numbers of adult grouse on each counting site in April with the numbers on each site in July (Figure 7.3). The linear regression of log July density on the previous log April density was:

Equation 7.4
ln July density = 0.362 + 0.722 ln April density

The standard error on the estimated slope was 0.092, giving a t-ratio for unit slope as t_{46}=–3.00, P<0.01. Thus, in summer, as in winter, there was good evidence of density-dependent loss of grouse. However, this analysis included both within- and between-site effects. Which of these was most important? Did areas with high April densities lose a higher percentage of birds (between-site effect), or did each site lose a higher percentage of birds when densities were high (within-site effect), or, as in winter, did both occur? Augmenting the above analysis by adding a year effect gave an estimated slope of 0.747 (SE=0.089), with a t-ratio for unit slope of t_{46}=2.84, P<0.01. The overall analysis, therefore, largely reflected the pattern of density dependence between sites. Differences between years were significant ($F_{3,43}$=2.84, P>0.01). If we dropped the year effect and added an individual site effect, we got an estimated slope of –0.144 (SE=0.200), giving a t-ratio for unit slope as t_{46}=5.72, P<0.001. Differences between sites were significant ($F_{3,43}$=2.83, P<0.01). The almost zero slope, which implied even stronger within-site

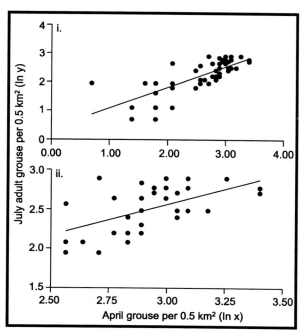

Figure 7.3 July grouse density at Langholm in relation to the previous April grouse density over the years 1992–96 on (i) each of the 0.5 km² counting sites, and (ii) the restricted set of 0.5 km² counting sites excluding sites 5, 6, 11 and 12. Data are ln-transformed

density dependence, may have merely reflected the small range of densities over the four years at each site. Thus, as in winter, the data were consistent with a single pattern of density dependence in summer loss which applied across sites within years and across years within sites.

As in winter, we refitted the regression model of log July density on the previous log April density after omitting sites 5, 6, 11 and 12 (Figure 7.3), which gave:

Equation 7.5
ln July density – 0.222 + 0.780 ln April density

The standard error on the estimated slope was 0.208, giving a t-ratio for unit slope as $t_{30}=-1.06$, $P>0.10$. The slopes of the two regression models were very similar, but the second was not significantly different from unit slope. This difference could be because of an effect of reduced sample size or it could be that evidence for density dependence in summer loss rested on including data from sites 5, 6, 11 and 12.

PATTERNS OF ADULT MORTALITY: RADIO-TAGGING

Estimating survival
Our second approach to investigate the rate of adult mortality was to radio-tag grouse and monitor their survival. Radio-tagging had two main advantages over grouse counts and carcase searching. First, it gave mortality rates which were unconfounded by counting errors and movements of grouse. Second, the date of death was accurately determined in most cases which allowed precise estimates of weekly survival. We captured and radio-tagged 130 grouse in October 1994, 135 grouse in September 1995, and 43 grouse in March 1996. An additional 40 radio-tagged grouse survived the first year and were re-entered into the survival analysis for the following year. Grouse were captured on a 50 km² area on the main moorland block. We located and flushed all of the radio-tagged grouse weekly and determined the proximate causes of mortality.

We calculated annual survival rates on the basis of a year beginning 1 October, including two seasonal intervals. Both winter

(1 October–31 March) and summer (1 April– 30 September) intervals were 26 weeks and coincided with the periods defined by the grouse counts. We used the Kaplan-Meier product limit method (Kaplin & Meier 1958) to estimate seasonal and annual survival, generalised to a staggered entry design (Pollock *et al.* 1989). We assumed that:
- birds were randomly sampled,
- survival times for individuals were independent,
- staggered entry individuals had survival distributions similar to previously marked birds,
- censoring mechanisms were independent of animal fate, and
- catching and tagging did not affect survival.

In a previous study we were unable to demonstrate any effect of these radio-tags on grouse survival and breeding success (Thirgood *et al.* 1995, Chapter 2). We right-censored birds whose fate was unknown because of radio failure or disappearance. We excluded from the survival analysis 25

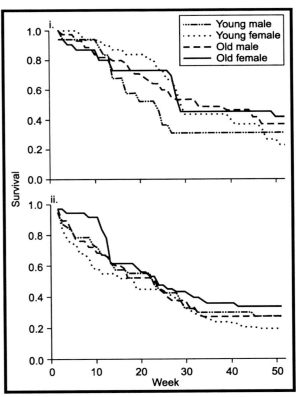

Figure 7.4 Weekly survival estimates of four age-sex classes of radio-tagged grouse at Langholm during (i) October 1994–September 1995; and (ii) October 1995– September 1996. Week 1 corresponds to the first week in October. Survival estimates are calculated using the Kaplin-Meier product limit method with a staggered entry modification

Table 7.5 Survival rates of radio-tagged grouse at Langholm during 1994–95 and 1995–96. Survival rates (S) and 95% confidence intervals (CI) calculated using the Kaplin-Meier product limit method with a staggered entry modification

Age-sex	1994–95		1995–96		Z	χ^2
	S	CI	S	CI		
Annual (Oct–Sept)						
Young male	0.314	0.106–0.522	0.281	0.126–0.437	0.245	0.011
Young female	0.230	0.067–0.392	0.199	0.114–0.284	0.331	0.627
Old male	0.370	0.226–0.514	0.280	0.146–0.414	0.897	1.846
Old female	0.418	0.237–0.598	0.346	0.209–0.484	0.609	0.389
Combined	0.338	0.253–0.424	0.264	0.204–0.325	1.338	3.537
Winter (Oct–Mar)						
Young male	0.366	0.150–0.582	0.438	0.282–0.594	0.537	0.075
Young female	0.671	0.510–0.832	0.433	0.330–0.537	2.380 *	3.203
Old male	0.598	0.455–0.741	0.409	0.275–0.544	1.890	2.941
Old female	0.731	0.569–0.893	0.463	0.311–0.616	2.351 *	3.595
Combined	0.609	0.524–0.694	0.436	0.370–0.502	3.159 **	7.898 **
Summer (Apr–Sept)						
Young male	0.857	0.598–1.116	0.641	0.391–0.893	1.170	0.768
Young female	0.343	0.121–0.565	0.460	0.299–0.620	0.833	0.346
Old male	0.618	0.431–0.806	0.684	0.467–0.902	0.450	0.062
Old female	0.571	0.360–0.783	0.738	0.564–0.932	1.231	2.193
Combined	0.556	0.441–0.671	0.606	0.504–0.707	0.634	0.451

Between-year differences in survival rate were tested using a two-tailed z-test statistic with significance denoted as: * P<0.05, ** P<0.01. Between-year differences in survival curves were tested using a log-rank test with significance of χ^2 denoted as: * P<0.05, ** P<0.01

birds that were found dead on their first radio-location. Birds that were radio-tagged in one year and survived into the next were censored on 30 September and reintroduced as new independent observations on 1 October. Differences in survival curves were tested using a log-rank test (White & Garrot 1990) and endpoint estimates of survival rate were tested using a two-tailed z-test statistic (Pollock *et al.* 1989).

Annual survival rates

We estimated annual survival curves and annual survival rates for each age-sex class of grouse (young male, young female, old male and old female) in both 1994–95 and 1995–96 (Figure 7.4, Table 7.5). Neither annual survival curves nor annual survival rates differed significantly between the age-sex classes within either year (Table 7.6). Similarly, comparisons of annual survival curves and annual survival rates within the four age-sex classes were not significantly different between years (Table 7.5). We then combined all age-sex classes for further analysis. The annual survival rate for all radio-tagged grouse combined was higher in 1994–95 (33.8%) than in 1995–96 (26.4%), but this difference was not significant (P>0.1, Figure 7.5, Table 7.5).

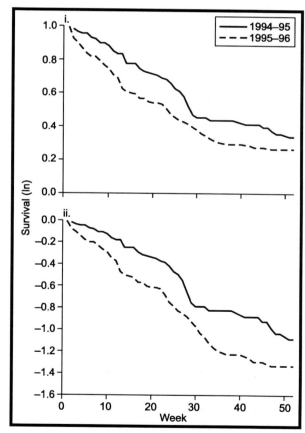

Figure 7.5 Weekly survival estimates of all age-sex classes of radio-tagged grouse combined at Langholm during October 1994–September 1995 and October 1995–September 1996. In (i) the survival estimates are calculated using the Kaplin Meier product limit method with a staggered entry modification and in (ii) the survival estimates are log-transformed. Week 1 corresponds to the first week in October

The graph in Figure 7.5i shows cumulative survival against time for all radio-tagged grouse in each of the two years of study. It provides a useful visual representation of the annual pattern of survival. However, to measure the survival rates we must plot the logarithm of survival against time (Figure 7.5ii) In this plot, the steepness of the line reflects the survival rate. Close examination of Figure 7.5 suggested three more or less distinct periods of mortality in the grouse population, marked by inflection points on the lines. The first period started in early October (week 1) and was characterised by a constant rate of survival until the end of February (week 22). The second period started in early March (week 23) and was characterised by a steep line inferring low survival. In 1994–95 the survival rate increased in late April (week 30), whereas in 1995–96 low survival rates continued until the end of May (week 34). The third period encompassed the remainder of the summer until the end of September (week 52) and in both years was characterised by relatively high adult survival rates. In 1994–95 there was a small decline in survival in mid-August (weeks 47–48) caused by shooting. It is noteworthy that the period of low survival in spring was bisected by the spring grouse counts and the subsequent division of winter and summer losses. Despite this discontinuity, we split the survival analysis by the spring grouse counts and investigated winter and summer survival for comparison with the count data.

Winter survival rates

Winter survival curves and survival rates for each age-sex class of grouse in 1994–95 and 1995–96 are shown in Figure 7.4 and Table 7.5. The survival of young males was significantly lower than either young or old females during the 1994–95 winter (Table 7.6). Examination of Figure 7.4 suggested that this difference was due to low survival of young males in the latter half of the winter. All other age-sex class comparisons of survival within either winter were not significantly different (Table 7.6). Comparison of winter survival of each age-sex class between years suggested that both young and old females survived better in the first winter than in the second (Table 7.5). These large differences in female survival between the two winters were the main cause of the winter survival rate of all radio-tagged grouse combined being higher in 1994–95 (60.9%) than in 1995–96 (43.6%) (P<0.01, Figure 7.5, Table 7.5). It should be noted in passing that it was possible for seasonal comparisons of survival rates and curves to yield statistically significant differences when annual comparisons including the same winter data did not. This was partly because survival rates in different seasons could counteract and also because survival estimates in summer were often based on smaller sample sizes which resulted in larger confidence limits.

Table 7.6 Age-sex class comparisons of survival curves and survival rates among grouse during 1994–95 and 1995–96. Survival calculated using the Kaplin-Meier product limit method with a staggered entry modification

	Survival curve (χ^2)			Survival rate (Z)		
1994–95						
Annual (Oct–Sept)						
	YF	OM	OF	YF	OM	OF
YM	0.299	0.682	1.567	0.622	0.436	0.738
YF	–	0.303	1.079	–	1.268	1.517
OM	–	–	0.274	–	–	0.404
Winter (Oct–Mar)						
	YF	OM	OF	YF	OM	OF
YM	4.738 *	2.320	4.981 *	2.224 *	1.761	2.640 *
YF	–	0.603	0.233	–	0.663	0.516
OM	–	–	1.307	–	–	1.206
Summer (Apr–Sept)						
	YF	OM	OF	YF	OM	OF
YM	3.653	1.057	1.279	2.949 *	1.464	1.672
YF	–	2.882	0.920	–	1.857	1.457
OM	–	–	0.256	–	–	0.326
1995–96						
Annual (Oct–Sept)						
	YF	OM	OF	YF	OM	OF
YM	0.867	0.001	0.762	0.907	0.012	0.616
YF	–	0.781	4.372*	–	0.995	1.786
OM	–	–	0.879	–	–	0.679
Winter (Oct–Mar)						
	YF	OM	OF	YF	OM	OF
YM	0.130	0.030	0.293	0.051	0.278	2.225
YF	–	0.002	0.815	–	0.281	0.317
OM	–	–	0.599	–	–	0.522
Summer (Apr–Sept)						
	YF	OM	OF	YF	OM	OF
YM	1.125	0.100	0.725	1.199	0.251	0.667
YF	–	1.994	4.671 *	–	1.630	2.314 *
OM	–	–	0.301	–	–	0.437

Differences in survival curves were tested using a log-rank test with significance of χ^2 denoted as: * P<0.05. Differences in survival rate were tested using a two-tailed z-test statistic with significance of Z denoted as: * P<0.05
YM young male, YF young female, OM old male, OF old female

Summer survival rates

Summer survival curves and summer survival rates for each age-sex class in 1995 and 1996 are shown in Figure 7.4 and Table 7.5. The summer survival curves are slightly misleading in that the y-intercepts for each age-sex class in week 27 should all be close to 1.0. Thus, for example, survival of young males in summer 1995 (85.7%) was higher than that of young females (34.3%), but both sexes had similar annual endpoint estimates of survival. Similarly, old female survival in summer 1996 was higher (73.8%) than young female survival (46.0%). Comparison of summer survival curves and rates within each age-sex class between years suggested that differences were not statistically significant (Table 7.5). Similarly, the summer survival rates of all age-sex classes combined did not differ significantly between 1995 (55.6%) and 1996 (60.6%) (P>0.5, Figure 7.5, Table 7.5). It is clear from Figure 7.5 that, in both years, most of the summer mortality occurred in early summer from weeks 27 to 34.

Estimating cause of mortality

Radio-tagging gave good estimates of the proximate cause of grouse mortality for two reasons.

- First, dead grouse were usually recovered irrespective of the cause of death.
- Second, grouse were usually recovered within a few days of death, and thus scavengers had relatively little time to hinder the identification of the cause.

We estimated the causes of mortality simply as the numbers of radio-tagged grouse killed by different types of predators in relation to the total number of dead radio-tagged grouse. This method excluded grouse which were right-censored in the preceding survival analysis through disappearance or radio failure, and thus slightly biased mortality rates upwards. This bias was more pronounced in 1995–96 (16 right-censored birds) than 1994–95 (4 right-censored birds), but increased estimates of mortality at most by 1.8%.

Causes of winter mortality

The great majority of deaths of radio-tagged grouse in both winters were attributable to raptors (Table 7.7), which accounted for a higher proportion of the recorded deaths in winter 1995–96 (82.0%) than in winter 1994–95 (72.3%) (raptor kills *versus* all other deaths: G=5.67, 1 df, P<0.025). Overall, the causes of winter mortality estimated by radio-tagging were similar to those estimated by carcase searching (Tables 7.3 & 7.7). Each method provided a check on the other.

Causes of summer mortality

Raptor predation was also the proximate cause of most mortality of radio-tagged adult grouse in each summer (Table 7.8), but accounted for a higher proportion of the recorded deaths in 1996 (94.7%) than in 1995 (66.7%) (raptor kills *versus* all other deaths: G=9.92, P<0.005), although this was partially due to higher shooting mortality in 1995. It is clear that raptors were responsible for virtually all the predation in April and May (weeks 27–34 in Figure 7.5). During this time, raptors accounted for 18

Table 7.7 Proximate causes of winter mortality among radio-tagged grouse at Langholm

	YM	YF	OM	OF	Total	% of total	% of deaths
1994–95							
Live 1 October	19	30	45	28	122	–	–
Dead 1 April	13	9	18	7	47	38.5	–
Raptor kill	9	5	16	4	31	27.9	72.3
Mammal kill	2	2	1	2	7	5.7	14.9
Other deaths	2	2	1	1	6	4.9	12.8
1995–96							
Live 1 October	40	30	48	35	153	–	–
Dead 1 April	23	18	29	19	89	58.2	–
Raptor kill	18	14	26	15	73	47.7	82.0
Mammal kill	2	3	2	3	10	6.5	11.2
Other deaths	3	1	1	1	6	3.9	6.7

YM young male, YF young female, OM old male, OF old female

Table 7.8 Proximate causes of summer mortality amoung radio-tagged grouse at Langholm

	YM	YF	OM	OF	Total	% of total	% of deaths
1995							
Live 1 April	6	20	26	21	73	–	–
Dead 1 October	1	13	10	9	33	45.2	–
Raptor kill	1	6	6	9	22	30.1	66.7
Mammal kill	0	2	1	0	3	4.1	9.1
Other deaths	0	2	1	0	3	4.1	9.1
Shot	0	3	2	0	5	6.8	15.2
1996							
Live 1 April	15	37	18	23	93	–	–
Dead 1 October	6	20	6	6	38	40.9	–
Raptor kill	5	20	6	5	36	38.7	94.7
Mammal kill	0	0	0	1	1	1.1	2.6
Other deaths	0	0	0	0	0	0	0
Shot	1	0	0	0	1	1.1	2.6

YM young male, YF young female, OM old male, OF old female

out of 21 deaths (85.7%) of radio-tagged grouse in 1995 and for 31 out of 32 (96.9%) in 1996.

PATTERNS OF GROUSE CHICK PREDATION

Grouse chick losses

Grouse chick losses were estimated by comparing the size of broods in the first week in June and in the third week in July. We knew from our radio-tagging studies that the median hatching date of grouse at Langholm was 28 May in 1995 (quartiles 25 May–3 June, N=27) and 30 May in 1996 (quartiles 25 May–2 June, N=33). Hence, the period of chick loss monitored was from one week to seven weeks old.

We found a minimum of 44 grouse broods with a pointing dog during the first week in June in each year 1993–96. Upon finding a brood, we searched for five minutes with the dog and captured and counted the chicks. June brood size thus represented a minimum

estimate because it was unlikely that all chicks were found in every case. We included hens without chicks as broods of zero. We found a minimum of 49 broods during the grouse counts in the third week in July in each of these years. We again included hens without chicks as broods of zero. July brood size was likely to be more accurate than June brood size as most grouse chicks flush and fly strongly at seven weeks. Estimated chick loss from June to July is therefore likely to be a minimum estimate. June and July brood size and percentage chick loss in each year are shown in Table 7.9. Brood size was significantly smaller in July than June in each year except 1993 (ANOVA: 1993 $F_{1,117}$=0.66, P=0.42; 1994 $F_{1,108}$=7.57, P=0.007; 1995 $F_{1,94}$=15.84, P=0.0001; 1996 $F_{1,102}$=14.78, P=0.0002). Chick loss from week 1 to week 7 ranged from 10% to 27% in the summers 1993–96.

We used the data on June and July brood sizes and the estimates of July grouse chick

Table 7.9 Estimates of grouse chick loss at Langholm during 1993–96. Data are from June brood counts and July grouse counts. Values are means±SE (sample size). June chick density is calculated as June brood size/July brood size x July chick density

Year	1993	1994	1995	1996
June brood size	3.98±0.44 (50)	5.57±0.34 (44)	6.58±0.32 (44)	5.91±0.26 (55)
July brood size	3.58±0.27 (68)	4.40±0.27 (67)	4.80±0.30 (55)	4.47±0.27 (49)
Chick loss %	10.1	21.0	27.0	24.4
June chicks per 0.5 km²	22.88	31.55	30.73	24.79
July chicks per 0.5 km²	20.58±3.04 (12)	24.92±4.54 (12)	22.42±3.50 (12)	18.75±2.51 (12)
Chick loss per 0.5 km²	2.30	6.63	8.31	6.04

7. Patterns of predation

Table 7.10 Estimates of grouse chick loss at Langholm during 1995–96. Data are from May brood size of radio-tagged hens and July grouse counts. Values are means±SE (sample size). May chick density is calculated as May brood size radio-tagged hens/July brood size x July chick density

Year	1995	1996
May brood size	8.36±0.42 (25)	8.50±0.42 (32)
July brood size	4.80±0.30 (55)	4.47±0.27 (49)
Chick loss %	42.6	47.4
May chicks per 0.5 km²	39.05	35.65
July chicks per 0.5 km²	22.42±3.50 (12)	18.75±2.51 (12)
Chick loss per 0.5 km²	16.63	16.90

density on our 12 0.5 km² counting sites to estimate June grouse chick density as: *June chick density* = June brood size/July brood size x July chick density. Estimates of June grouse chick density in years 1993–96 are given in Table 7.9 for comparison with July chick density as determined by counts with pointing dogs. These estimates suggested that losses from the first week in June to the third week in July varied from 2.3 to 8.3 chicks per 0.5 km² in the summers 1993–96.

Estimates of June grouse chick density were derived from measures of June brood size, by which time brood reduction has already occurred. The brood size at hatch of radio-tagged hens, measured as the number of eggs that hatched, was significantly larger than the brood size of randomly located hens during the first week in June as determined by searching for chicks with pointing dogs (brood size RT hens: 1995 8.36±0.42, 1996 8.50±0.42; brood size random hens: 1995 6.58±0.32, 1996 5.9±0.26; ANOVA: 1995 $F_{1,63}$=11.72, P<0.001, 1996 $F_{1,85}$=42.0, P<0.001). This result suggested a mean loss of 1.8 and 2.6 chicks per brood between hatch and the first brood counts in the two years.

We recalculated grouse chick losses for 1995 and 1996 using the mean brood size at hatch of radio-tagged hens in late May for comparison with mean size of random broods during grouse counts in the third week in July (Table 7.10). Chick loss from week 0 to week 7 averaged 45% in summers 1995–96. We used the data on May and July brood sizes and the estimates

of July grouse chick density on our counting sites to estimate May grouse chick density at chick hatch as: *May grouse chick density* = May brood size radio-tagged hens/July brood size x July chick density. Estimates of May chick density in 1995–96 are given in Table 7.10 for comparison with July chick density. Chick loss between these periods averaged 16.8 chicks per 0.5 km².

Were grouse chick losses density dependent?
To check for evidence of density dependence in patterns of chick loss, we compared July hen density against July chick density for each counting site in each year (Figure 7.6). Essentially, this analysis tested whether the young/hen ratio changed in relation to hen density. The linear regression of log July chick density on July hen density was:

Equation 7.6
ln July chick density = 1.278 + 1.089 ln July hen density

The standard error on the estimated slope was 0.070, giving a t-ratio for unit slope as t_{46}=1.27, P>0.2. Therefore, on this basis, there was no evidence for density-dependent changes in the young/hen ratio and no suggestion of density-dependent chick loss.

DISCUSSION
In this Chapter we have presented information on the changes in grouse numbers and the patterns of predation observed at Langholm during 1992–96. The first point to stress is that, allowing for the seasonal fluctuations, the Langholm grouse population was fairly stable from year to year during this five-year period. It showed no significant upward or downward trends in the counts for April, July or October.

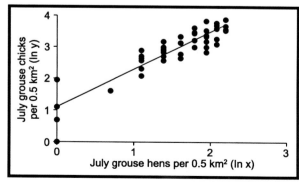

Figure 7.6 July chick density in relation to July hen density on each of the 0.5 km² counting areas over the years 1992–96. Data are ln-transformed

Nonetheless, the local variation was considerable, as shown by the densities on individual counting sites.

Our data from the grouse counts suggested that, on average, grouse numbers were 33% lower in April than in the previous October. In each year, however, more grouse were found dead on the counting sites than expected from the difference in counts of live birds between October and April, suggesting net immigration on to the count sites. We do not know where these immigrants came from, but suspect that they came from low-density peripheral areas of the moor where we did not systematically count grouse. These estimates of winter loss were similar to those found in previous studies of red grouse, in Glen Esk (Jenkins *et al.* 1963, 1964), Kerloch (Jenkins *et al.* 1967; Watson *et al.* 1984), Yorkshire (Hudson 1986a) and Strathspey (Hudson 1992). The first three of these areas supported few predators and the last many.

Mammalian predators were killed by gamekeepers at Langholm and most grouse found dead on our counting sites in winter were killed by raptors. On average, raptors were the proximate cause of 70% of the observed winter mortality of grouse and they killed the equivalent of 30% of the grouse counted in October. Raptor predation at Langholm was more important relative to other causes of winter mortality than in previous red grouse studies. Using similar techniques, Jenkins *et al.* (1964) demonstrated that raptors and foxes killed roughly equal numbers of grouse during winter in Glen Esk. More recently, Hudson, Newborn and Robertson (1997) collected grouse carcasses using identical techniques to ourselves from six sites in Strathspey and four sites in Yorkshire over the period 1986–95. Raptor predation was responsible for 52% of deaths in Strathspey and for 42% in Yorkshire, with foxes responsible for most of the remainder in Strathspey and a combination of foxes, stoats and parasites for the remainder in Yorkshire.

Winter losses were density dependent, in that proportionally more grouse were lost from high-density sites than low-density

sites. There was a single pattern of density dependence in winter loss which applied both across sites within years and across years within sites. In other words, sites with high grouse densities consistently lost a higher proportion of grouse than other sites, but each site also showed a tendency to lose more grouse in years when its grouse density was high. Winter losses as measured here incorporate both winter kills and unexplained losses or gains assumed to represent net movement of grouse. Our analysis of density dependence was unable to separate these two components of loss. However, whilst the numbers of both raptor kills and mammal kills found overwinter on counting sites increased with October grouse density, the ratio of raptor/mammal kills also increased with grouse density, suggesting that raptors rather than foxes could have been supplying much of the density dependence in winter loss. This fits with what we know about winter foraging in harriers and peregrines in relation to grouse density (Chapter 4). It also makes sense in terms of probable fox densities and local patterns of fox control. Most foxes at Langholm were killed on low ground and fox densities were typically higher in this habitat than on moorland (Hewson 1986).

Differences in the numbers of adult grouse counted between April and July at Langholm suggested that on average 30% of adult grouse disappeared during this period. Such high losses of adult grouse in summer were not found in the early studies in Glen Esk and Kerloch (Jenkins *et al.* 1963, 1964, 1967; Watson *et al.* 1984), neither were they reported in the recent studies in Yorkshire and Strathspey (Hudson 1986a, 1992). However, recent work at Rickarton in NE Scotland revealed that 38% of radio-tagged hens were lost, mostly due to fox predation, between March and June (Moss *et al.* 1990). Moss *et al.* (1990) suggested that the difference between this study and the previous work in NE Scotland was due to the abundance of foxes at Rickarton. In a later publication, Moss *et al.* (1996) concluded that the demographic patterns were not consistent with the hypothesis that decreased hen survival was sufficient to cause the observed cyclic decline in grouse density.

Summer losses of adult grouse at Langholm were density dependent in that proportionally more grouse were lost between April and July from high-density sites than low-density sites. As in winter, there appeared to be a single pattern of density dependence which applied both across sites within years and across years within sites. We did not conduct carcase searching throughout the summer and therefore cannot comment on spatial variation in the causes of summer loss.

The radio-tagging study provided an independent method of assessing the rates and causes of grouse mortality at Langholm and, as such, provided a check on the conclusions derived from the counts and carcase searches. More importantly, it also gave precise estimates of the timing of grouse mortality, as most birds were recovered shortly after death. In general, differences in survival between age and sex classes were low and not statistically significant. Not surprisingly, where differences did occur, young birds tended to have lower survival than old birds. Annual survival rates for all age and sex classes together, estimated from two years of radio-tagging, suggested that, on average, 30% of grouse survived from one October to the next. This survival estimate was similar to those calculated from recoveries of ringed grouse [33% Glen Esk 1957–61 (Jenkins *et al*. 1963); 34% Yorkshire 1979–85 (Hudson 1986a)] and from observations of back-tabbed grouse [(29% Glen Esk 1957–61 (Jenkins *et al*. 1963)]. It should be noted that proportionally more grouse were shot in Glen Esk and Yorkshire than at Langholm.

The radio-tagging demonstrated that, whilst mortality rates were consistently high throughout both the winters of study, there was a marked increase in mortality during spring, from March to April in 1995 and from March to May in 1996. This period of high spring mortality of adults was followed by relatively low mortality during the summer, with the exception of some shooting losses in 1995. Why was mortality especially high during the spring? Possible explanations are that this was a period when grouse were re-establishing territories and were therefore especially vulnerable to predation, and that it coincided with the time when both harriers and peregrines returned to the moor to breed and were present at greater densities than in winter. Comparable estimates of the seasonal patterns of mortality derived from other radio-tagging studies of red grouse were not currently available. However, the number of grouse carcases recovered monthly over ten years on ten sites in Strathspey and Yorkshire also peaked in March and April (Hudson *et al*. 1997).

The radio-tagging gave estimates of the rates and causes of winter mortality that were similar to those obtained by counts and carcase searching. Overall, 61% of radio-tagged grouse survived the first winter and 44% survived the second. As found for the grouse recovered dead during carcase searching, the proximate cause of death during winter of the majority of radio-tagged grouse was raptor predation. The proportion of radio-tagged grouse at Langholm killed by raptors was higher than that found in a smaller sample of radio-tagged grouse in Strathspey (Hudson 1992).

Radio-tagging during the summer suggested that 56% of adult grouse survived the first summer and 61% the second. Most mortality occurred during April and May, although there were some later shooting losses in 1995. One third of all radio-tagged adult grouse were killed during the period of high mortality in April and May, and 90% of these birds were killed by raptors. The similarity between this estimate of mortality during spring and the observed difference in adult grouse numbers between the April and July counts strongly suggested that most losses were due to predation by raptors rather than to emigration of grouse from our counting sites.

We produced two separate estimates of grouse chick loss by comparing the size of grouse broods recorded during the July grouse counts with brood size of radio-tagged hens at hatch in late May and of randomly located hens in early June. These comparisons suggested that chick losses at Langholm from the first week in June until the third week in July ranged from 10% to 27% in the summers 1993–96. These figures compared with chick losses recorded over the same six-week period in Perthshire and

Strathspey in the presence of breeding harriers of 21% and 17% respectively (Redpath 1991). Brood reduction had already occurred by the time grouse were one week old and chick losses from hatch until July averaged 45% in the two years for which we have data.

There was no evidence of density dependence in the ratio of grouse chicks/adult female grouse during the July brood counts, suggesting that summer losses of grouse chicks did not vary in relation to grouse density. Caution must be taken in interpreting this result because several density-dependent or inverse density-dependent processes could occur simultaneously and effectively cancel each other out. For instance, hens on low-density sites could produce smaller clutches or their chicks could starve, whereas hens on high-density sites could lose more chicks to predators. As we have little information on spatial variation in clutch size, hatching success and causes of chick mortality, we cannot distinguish between these hypotheses.

Throughout this Chapter, we have presented data on the patterns of predation and other losses observed in the Langholm grouse population. We have not commented on the impact of predation and other losses on either the numbers of grouse available for shooting in autumn or on breeding densities in spring. These issues are addressed in the next Chapter.

Chapter 8

Male grouse chasing a hen harrier male away from its brood

8. Impact of predation

- Raptors killed on average 30% of the grouse population during October–March but we were unable to determine the extent to which this predation reduced breeding densities in spring.
- Winter predation affected territorial as well as non-territorial grouse, and observations in 1996–97 suggested that there were 21% fewer territorial males in April than in the previous October.
- Raptor predation in winter could have been partially compensated through movement of grouse or through reduced losses to mammalian predators or parasites.
- Grouse were killed in winter by harriers, peregrines and occasionally other raptors, but we were unable to determine the relative importance of the different species.
- Raptors killed on average 30% of the adult grouse population during April–June and this predation was unlikely to have been compensated by reduced losses from other causes over the same period.
- Most grouse were territorial by April, and there was little scope for late replacement of breeding females killed by raptors.
- Summer predation of adult grouse was due to harriers, peregrines and occasionally other raptors, but again we were unable to determine the relative importance of the different species.
- Harrier predation in 1995 and 1996 reduced grouse chick density by approximately 37%. These losses were largely in addition to unexplained losses of 17% which occurred within a few days of hatch.
- The data were strongly suggestive that summer predation on adult grouse and chicks by raptors was largely additive, and during 1995 and 1996 reduced the post-breeding density by 50%.
- A model combining the estimated reduction in autumn grouse densities caused by raptors with the observed density dependence in winter loss predicted that, in the absence of summer raptor predation, spring grouse densities would increase within two years to a level 1.3 times that found in the presence of raptors. Similarly, the model predicted that breeding production in the absence of raptors would increase within two years to a level 2.5 times that found in the presence of raptors. This model was applicable only to the high ratio of raptors/grouse found at Langholm and, with a lower raptor/grouse ratio, the impact would have been predicted as much lower.

INTRODUCTION

In the preceding Chapters, we presented estimates of the numbers of grouse taken by raptors and the observed patterns of predation in the grouse population. Demonstrating that raptors removed many grouse, and that a substantial proportion of the grouse population was killed by raptors in any one year, did not necessarily mean that raptor predation was limiting grouse numbers. Raptor predation could have been compensated by reduced competition within the grouse population for limiting resources such as food or territories, or by the reduced effect of other density-dependent losses, such as movement, predation by mammals or disease. In this Chapter we investigate the extent to which mortality of grouse caused by raptors at Langholm was additional to (rather than replaced) mortality due to other factors. Many of the data were presented in earlier Chapters, but we also introduce new information on the effect of territorial status and parasite burdens on survival. We investigate the extent of compensation in both winter and summer predation in an attempt to find whether raptor predation reduced breeding density of grouse in spring and the numbers of grouse available for shooting in autumn. Finally, we develop a simple model to investigate the longer-term consequences of raptor predation on the Langholm grouse population.

WINTER PREDATION

Compensation of winter raptor predation could occur through a number of mechanisms. First, if most winter predation fell on non-territorial grouse, as has been shown elsewhere (Jenkins *et al.* 1963; Watson 1985), then winter predation would be largely compensatory. Second, if winter predation fell on territorial grouse, but there remained a pool of non-territorial birds from which replacement birds could be drawn (Watson & Moss 1990), then some compensation could occur. Finally, if increased grouse densities were to result from reduced raptor predation, then partial compensation could occur through increased mammalian predation or increased parasite burdens (Hudson 1986a, b; Hudson *et al.* 1992a, b). If any of these conditions held, then raptor predation overwinter need not have reduced breeding numbers or success.

Territorial status and winter survival of radio-tagged grouse

We investigated the effect of territorial status on winter survival by using data from radio-tagged grouse. Grouse were radio-tagged in September–October of 1994 and 1995 and were located weekly until April or until they died or disappeared. We did not conduct detailed observations on territorial behaviour of individual grouse as described by Watson (1985). Instead, we defined male grouse as territorial if >50% of radio-locations during October–December were within an area of <25 ha, and female grouse as territorial if the bird was paired on >50% of radio-locations during this same period. Such definitions are, of course, arbitrary but we could apply them with rigour to our data. We included only those grouse for which we had a minimum of ten radio-locations during the period

October–December. Thus, we had to exclude those grouse which died between October and December because we had insufficient data to determine their territorial status. The extent to which predation fell on radio-tagged grouse before 1 January varied between the two winters (see Chapter 7). In 1994–95, eight of 17 females and 11 of 30 males which died in the winter died during October–December. In 1995–96, equivalent figures were 26 of 37 females and 33 of 52 males.

The effect of territorial status in October–December on the survival of radio-tagged male grouse in January–March is shown in Table 8.1. In both winters, all radio-tagged male grouse that were alive on 1 January were territorial during the previous October–December. On average, 64% of these males subsequently survived until the following April. The effect of territorial status on the survival of radio-tagged female grouse was more complex (Table 8.1). In both winters, the majority of female grouse alive on 1 January were territorial in the previous October–December. We combined the data for the two winters for statistical analysis because sample sizes were small. Survival until the following April of territorial females (79%) tended to be higher than that of non-territorial females (69%), but this difference was not statistically significant (G-test: G=0.67, 1 df, P>0.25).

Our radio-tagging data suggested that much mortality during January–March fell on territorial grouse. Assuming that we captured and radio-tagged a random sample of the grouse available each autumn, our data also suggested that few non-territorial grouse, in particular few non-territorial males, remained alive by 1 January. By implication, there may have been only limited scope for compensation of mortality in the period January–March. Our data did not allow us to say whether grouse killed between October and December were territorial or non-territorial. Furthermore, even assuming that territorial birds were killed during October–December, we had no information regarding the numbers of non-territorial birds which could, in theory, have replaced them in the territorial (future breeding) population. Therefore, we cannot comment on the likely

Table 8.1 Territorial status in October–December and survival of male and female radio-tagged grouse during January–March

Territorial status	Survival	1995	1996
Territorial male	Survive	33	34
	Die	19	19
Non-territorial male	Survive	0	0
	Die	0	0
Territorial female	Survive	34	21
	Die	8	7
Non-territorial female	Survive	5	6
	Die	1	4

extent of compensation of mortality during October–December. Because an average of 55% of the observed winter mortality of radio-tagged grouse occurred during October–December, this weakened our ability to use the radio-tagging data to draw firm conclusions regarding the effect of winter predation on spring breeding densities, but predation during January–March could not have been fully compensated.

Territory counting and winter survival

Central to the issue of winter compensation was the question of whether or not the numbers of territorial males present in April were determined in the previous October (Watson & Moss 1990). On this view, if the numbers of territorial males were lower in April than October, then at least some of the winter mortality must have been additive. We investigated this question by counting the numbers of displaying male grouse on six sites at Langholm in October 1996 and again in April 1997. The territory counting sites varied in size from 1 km² to 2 km²; each was chosen to afford good visibility from vantage points and to encompass one of the regular 0.5 km² grouse counting sites. We counted the numbers of displaying males at each site at dawn on three days during the first week in October and on three days during the first week in April. Observations were conducted from vantage points at various locations within the sites, and displaying males were considered to be those which gave territorial calls or were seen in song flight (Watson & Jenkins 1964). We concentrated on counting displaying males rather than determining

territory boundaries. We compared the change in numbers of displaying males to the change in numbers of grouse counted during our routine counts with pointing dogs.

The numbers of displaying male grouse on each territory counting site in October and April are shown in Table 8.2. There was considerable variation between sites in the overwinter change in numbers of displaying males, but on average 21% fewer territorial males were counted in April than in the previous October. Comparison of the numbers of grouse counted with pointing dogs on a subsample of these sites suggested that winter losses averaged 31%. There were considerable differences in the percentage change in displaying males overwinter and the percentage change in grouse numbers overwinter within individual sites; there was also no clear relationship between losses of displaying males or total numbers of grouse and October grouse density. Taken in total, these results suggested that some winter loss of territorial males did occur, but that there was great spatial variation in the extent of this loss.

Compensation through movement of grouse

One possible mechanism for compensation of winter predation was movement of grouse, in that birds lost to predators might have been replaced by immigrants from elsewhere. The data presented in Chapter 7 demonstrated that winter loss of grouse, defined as the difference between October density and April density, was influenced by the numbers of grouse that were killed in winter and a residual unexplained change in numbers, assumed to represent net immigration of grouse into our counting sites.

In interpreting these findings, the assumption was made that predation and movement did not occur at the same time. Consider a counting site in which 50 grouse were counted in October, 20 grouse were found dead and 40 grouse were counted in April. Two conclusions could be drawn, representing the opposite extremes of a continuum. One conclusion could be that ten grouse moved into the study area in early winter, increasing the population to 60

Table 8.2 Numbers of displaying male grouse on six territory counting areas in October 1996 and April 1997 compared with the numbers of grouse counted with pointing dogs on grouse counting sites. Territory counting sites varied in size from 1 km² to 2 km². Grouse counting sites were 0.5 km² and were located within the territory counting sites

Area	Displaying males Oct	Apr	% change	Grouse count Oct	Apr	% change
1	18	20	+11	36	12	–67
2	21	15	–29	29	17	–41
3	24	14	–42	16	20	+25
4	22	18	–18	29	25	–14
5	27	16	–41	30	18	–40
6	16	15	–6	12	6	–50
Mean			–21			–31

and then predators killed 20 grouse resulting in a net loss of 20 breeding birds. An alternative could be that predators killed 20 of the original 50 grouse early in the winter and then ten grouse moved into the vacancies thus created, resulting in a net loss of only ten breeding birds. In the first scenario, predation was 100% additive, whilst in the second 50% of the predation was compensated, within the counting site, by immigration.

It is clear from the above that conclusions regarding compensatory mortality in winter will differ depending upon whether predation or movement occurred first. Radio-tagging studies of natal dispersal in Strathspey demonstrated that most movement occurred in September–December (Hudson 1992). We have already demonstrated at Langholm that predation occurred at a constant rate throughout the winter and peaked in spring (Chapter 7), and that few non-territorial grouse were still alive after 1 January to replace breeding birds which were subsequently killed. However, we could use the two scenarios described above to estimate the likely extreme values of compensation and additivity in winter between which the true value was likely to lie.

Data for this analysis came from the counts of grouse in October and April, the number of winter kills recovered during carcase searching, and the unexplained losses or gains assumed to represent net movement of grouse for each counting site at Langholm over the four winters of the study (Chapter 7). We expressed the number of grouse lost to the population from either predation or movement as k values which were the differences between log population densities at the start and end of a period of time. k values were more useful than percentages dying or moving because they avoided some of the statistical distortions involved in the use of percentages and different k values could be summed to give total values of mortality.

In the first scenario, movement occurred before predation. For each counting site in each winter, we calculated:

k losses to movement = log (October density) – log (October density – movement)

k losses to predation = log (October density – movement) – log (April density)

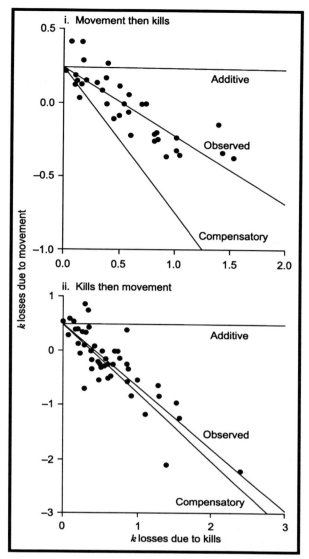

Figure 8.1 Plots of k losses due to kills against k losses due to movement during winter at Langholm. In (i) movement occurs before kills; in (ii) kills occur before movement. The lines for total additivity assume that increasing kills do not influence movement and therefore have slopes of 0. The lines for total compensation assume that increasing kills are matched by decreased movement and therefore have slopes of –1.0. The observed line is the regression through the data points for each counting site in each year. It suggests that overwinter losses were partly compensated by net immigration (up to 50% in (i) and 95% in (ii)) (see text for further details)

In Figure 8.1i we plotted k losses to predation against k losses to movement. The line for total additivity assumed that increasing losses due to predation did not influence gains or losses to movement, and therefore had zero slope. The line for total compensation assumed that increasing losses to predation resulted in identical numbers gained through movement, and therefore had a slope of –1.00. The observed regression line through the real data suggested that 55% of the winter predation was compensated by movement. In other words, for every two grouse killed in the winter, the spring breeding population was reduced by one.

In the second scenario, predation occurred before movement. For each counting site in each winter we calculated:

k losses to predation = log (October density) – log (October density – winter predation)

k losses to movement = log (October density – winter predation) – log (April density)

In Figure 8.1ii we plotted k losses to predation against k losses to movement. The lines for total additivity and total compensation were drawn as before, with slopes of zero and –1.00 respectively. The observed regression line through the real data suggested that 95% of the winter predation was compensated by movement. In other words, for every 20 grouse killed in the winter, the spring breeding population was reduced by 1.

Neither of the plots in Figure 8.1 is a true reflection of what happened in the grouse population. In reality, predation and movement were likely to have occurred at the same time, at least in the first half of the winter. However, the plots gave us two extreme values between which the true extent of compensation of winter predation was likely to have fallen. This suggested that between 55% and 95% of winter predation on the count sites could have been compensated by ingress of grouse from elsewhere.

A major caveat should be attached to the foregoing conclusion. The analysis was conducted at the scale of the individual counting site and reflected compensation of predation through movement of grouse into that counting site. The analysis did not reflect compensation at the scale of the wider population. At this larger scale, compensation of predation through movement, as calculated above, depended upon the assumption that formerly non-territorial grouse would not have bred had they not moved and become territorial. This assumption has not been tested.

Compensation at the population level could also occur if movement of grouse, as a result of the death of others, resulted in increased breeding success of the bird which moved. Subsequent chick survival could increase if a female grouse moved from a poor territory to a good territory which became vacant due to predation. Whilst predation reduced the breeding population by one female, the increased breeding success of the female which moved could partially compensate this mortality. Currently, we do not know enough about the influence of habitat quality on breeding success to determine to what extent this mechanism could operate.

Compensation through mammalian predation
Another way in which winter predation by raptors could be partially compensated is if increased grouse densities in the absence of raptors resulted in higher rates of predation by mammals such as foxes. However, there was no evidence that fox predation of grouse was density dependent at Langholm. In fact, there was a trend for a lower proportion of grouse to be killed by foxes on high-density sites (Chapter 7). There were two factors which could explain the lack of density dependence in fox predation. First, analysis of fox scats collected at Langholm suggested that the winter diet of foxes was influenced by the abundance of field voles rather than of grouse (F M Leckie *et al.*, unpublished data). Fox scats more frequently contained voles when voles were relatively abundant, but did not contain more grouse when grouse were relatively abundant. Thus, we had no evidence that individual foxes ate more grouse when grouse were more abundant. Second, unlike raptors, foxes at Langholm were controlled by gamekeepers. Hence, the numbers of foxes were more likely to reflect the extent of fox control than prey abundance.

With only five years of data, it is possible that density-dependent fox predation occurred without us detecting it. Furthermore, it is possible that fox predation could be density dependent in the absence of raptors, but not in the presence of raptors. Finally, whilst density dependence influenced the strength of compensation, it was still possible for losses which were not density dependent to compensate to some extent.

We could calculate a minimum estimate of compensation of winter raptor predation through increased mammal predation, assuming that mammal predation was not density dependent. From the data in Chapter 7 we know that, on average, raptors killed 30% and mammals killed 10% of the grouse population counted in October by the following April. Assuming a constant rate of predation, mammals would also kill 10% of the grouse which survived in the absence of raptor predation. Therefore, even in the absence of density-dependent mammal predation, 10% of winter raptor predation might have been compensated by increased mammal predation.

Compensation through parasitism

One further mechanism for compensation of winter raptor predation is through the density-dependent effects of parasites. Red grouse are hosts for a number of parasites, of which the most important is the caecal threadworm *Trichostrongylus tenuis*. The red grouse/*T. tenuis* system has been the subject of intensive study by Hudson (Hudson 1986a, b, 1992; Hudson *et al.* 1992a, b; Dobson & Hudson 1992, 1995). This parasitic nematode inhabits the caecal sacs of the grouse and has a direct life cycle with no intermediate hosts. Experiments have demonstrated that the parasite reduces both the survival and fecundity of the grouse. Modelling suggested that the effects of the parasite on grouse breeding success were sufficient to produce the cyclical fluctuations seen in some grouse populations. Parasite-induced mortality of adult grouse may be either direct through loss of condition or indirect through increased susceptibility of infected individuals to predators. Current knowledge of the red grouse/*T. tenuis* system indicates that worm burdens increase following years of high grouse density. Thus, if reduced raptor predation resulted in higher grouse densities, then it would seem possible that parasite-induced mortality could increase, at least in certain years.

We collected a sample of 123 grouse which were killed by predators, mainly raptors, in the months October–March during 1992–96. We did not collect samples from birds which died from other causes. Grouse were aged and sexed on plumage characteristics. Many of the grouse (83 of 123) had been radio-tagged and were therefore aged and sexed when alive. The remainder included only those corpses for which accurate age and sex classification could be made. Estimation of parasite burdens followed established procedures (see Chapter 2, Hudson 1986a).

Worm burdens were low in all age and sex classes of grouse at Langholm (Table 8.3). Intensive studies on English moors suggested that body condition and fecundity of female grouse started to decline when parasite burdens reached 3000 worms per bird, but the general applicability of this threshold to grouse populations elsewhere is currently unknown. Worm burdens at Langholm during 1992–96 were considerably lower than this threshold, and it therefore seems unlikely that parasites had much influence on grouse demography. However, if the grouse population were to increase in the absence of raptors, it is quite possible that parasite-induced reductions in survival and fecundity would occur. At the current time we do not understand sufficiently well the dynamics of the red grouse/*T. tenuis* system at low grouse densities to predict at what grouse density this would occur, to what extent the worm burdens would increase, or the effect on grouse survival and breeding production.

Did winter predation reduce spring breeding density?

The data from grouse counts, carcase searches and radio-tagging all suggested that on average 40% of the October grouse population at Langholm were killed during the winter by the combined action of raptors and mammalian carnivores. The key question was whether or not this predation reduced spring breeding densities.

The radio-tagging data suggested that winter predation was not restricted to non-territorial grouse, at least from January to March. Thus, we had no evidence that territorial status influenced overwinter survival. This was supported by the observed reduction in the numbers of displaying males counted in October 1996 and in the following April.

Table 8.3 Level of *Trichostrongylus tenuis* infection in grouse killed by predators in winter at Langholm during 1992–96. Figures show geometric mean worm burden with 95% confidence intervals and sample sizes. Worm burdens are estimated using techniques described by Hudson (1986a)

Age-sex class	Sample size	Geometric mean	95% CI
Young male	43	70	68–72
Young female	23	57	55–59
Old male	30	164	162–166
Old female	27	196	194–198

Potential for compensation of winter predation was greatest through the movement of grouse, and analysis at the scale of the counting site suggested that 55–95% of winter predation could be compensated in this way. However, at the scale of the wider population, compensation through movement of grouse was largely dependent on the assumption that grouse which moved would not have bred had they not moved. There was scope for some compensation of winter raptor predation through increased predation by mammals, depending on the strength of density-dependent mammalian predation. Compensation through density-dependent parasite-induced mortality or reduced breeding success was also possible, although this was most likely to occur at grouse densities higher than currently found at Langholm.

In the light of the above, it seemed premature to draw firm conclusions regarding the extent to which winter predation by raptors and other predators reduced spring breeding densities at Langholm. However, given certain assumptions, it was possible to estimate the extreme values between which the true extent of compensation was likely to occur.

Which raptors were responsible for the winter predation?

We were unable to distinguish between the kills of different species of raptors on the basis of the field signs left at grouse carcases (Chapter 2, S J Thirgood, S M Redpath & P J Hudson 1997). We were also unable to estimate the numbers of grouse killed by the different species of raptors in winter (Chapter 6), because it was difficult to estimate the numbers of individual raptors hunting the moor during winter (Chapter 3) and because our analysis of raptor diet in winter was based on pellets which were not suited to assessing predation rates (Chapter 5). Therefore, although in each winter we saw many more harriers than peregrines per 100 hours of fieldwork (Chapter 3), we could not say that harriers killed more grouse in winter than did peregrines. In fact, between-species comparisons of sighting frequency of raptors were relatively meaningless, because different foraging techniques made harriers more visible than peregrines. In summary, we could not reliably apportion winter predation of grouse between harriers, peregrines or other raptors.

SUMMER PREDATION

Summer predation of adult grouse

Counts and radio-tagging suggested that predation, primarily by raptors, reduced adult grouse density at Langholm by 30% between April and June. Did this predation reduce grouse productivity or did compensation reduce the impact of the loss? There were a number of compensatory mechanisms which could have reduced the importance of summer raptor predation.

- If predation fell on non-territorial grouse, or if non-territorial grouse were available to replace territorial grouse which were killed, then predation up to a certain point in the season could be compensated.
- Density-dependent losses of adults or chicks to other predators, disease or starvation could increase if grouse densities increased as a result of reduced raptor predation.

Territorial status and summer predation

In the summers of 1995 and 1996, we monitored the survival and breeding success of radio-tagged female grouse. In both years, a high percentage of these females was killed by raptors during April and May (Chapter 7). Whilst we were unable to follow the breeding success of all radio-tagged females until their chicks fledged, we were able to ascertain whether or not each female still alive in May attempted to breed. In both 1995 and 1996, all radio-tagged female grouse laid a clutch of eggs (Table 8.4). This suggested that all these females were territorial and paired by May, and that no radio-tagged females were non-territorial.

We could also investigate this question with an independent data set from the April grouse counts conducted at Langholm during 1993–96. On these counts, we distinguished between female grouse which were found paired with males and females which were

Table 8.4 Spring survival and breeding status of radio-tagged female grouse at Langholm during 1995 and 1996. Breeding status is defined by production of clutch

Year	Live 1 April	Live 1 July	Attempted breeding	No attempted breeding
1995	42	27	27	0
1996	61	40	40	0

Table 8.5 Status of female grouse found by pointing dogs during April counts at Langholm 1993–96

Year	Females in pairs	Females unpaired
1993	83	2
1994	102	1
1995	86	0
1996	77	1

alone and presumably unpaired. On average, 99% of the females counted were paired (Table 8.5). These observations suggested that by April virtually all female grouse at Langholm were attempting to breed and that there would therefore be very limited scope for the replacement of territorial females which were subsequently killed.

Compensation through mammalian predation

Raptor predation of adult grouse in summer could be partially compensatory if increased grouse densities in the absence of raptors resulted in higher rates of predation by mammals. However, the likelihood of this occurring in summer seemed less than in winter. As described above, there was no evidence that mammalian predation of adult grouse was density dependent. This may have been because foxes did not appear to demonstrate a functional response to grouse or because their numbers were controlled by gamekeepers. Alternatively, it may be that our data were insufficient to detect density dependence even if it did occur. Furthermore, it is possible that density-dependent mammalian predation could occur if higher grouse densities resulted from the absence of raptors. Most importantly, however, mammals were responsible for only a tiny proportion of the observed predation of radio-tagged grouse between April and June.

We could calculate an estimate of compensation of summer raptor predation through increased mammalian predation assuming that mammalian predation was not density dependent. We knew that, on average, raptors killed 30% and mammals killed 3% of the April grouse population by the end of June. Assuming a constant rate of predation, mammals would have also killed 3% of the grouse which survived in the absence of raptor predation. On this basis, only 3% of summer raptor predation would

have been compensated by mammalian predation.

Compensation through parasitism

A further mechanism for partial compensation of summer predation on adult grouse was through density-dependent losses due to the parasite *T. tenuis*. These losses could be either direct through adult mortality or indirect through reduced fecundity. As already described, *T. tenuis* can reduce the survival and fecundity of grouse and its effects are more severe following years of high grouse density. Worm counts conducted on grouse killed during the winter by predators at Langholm revealed that worm burdens were considerably lower than the threshold level at which the body condition and fecundity of grouse decline (Table 8.3). However, these thresholds refer to grouse in northern England and their applicability to Langholm is unknown. Furthermore, we do not currently know to what extent worm burdens would increase if grouse densities increased, and the effect of this increase on grouse productivity.

Compensation of adult predation through density-dependent chick mortality

An indirect compensatory mechanism which could reduce the impact of summer predation of adult grouse is any form of density-dependent chick mortality. Thus, if reduced predation resulted in higher breeding densities and higher chick density, would chick mortality increase accordingly? We demonstrated in Chapter 7 that the ratio of young grouse/adult females during the July counts was not density dependent. In other words, summer losses of grouse chicks did not vary in relation to grouse density, at least over the range of densities observed at Langholm.

Summer predation of grouse chicks

In this section we investigate how much of the chick losses can be accounted for by harrier predation and then consider compensatory mechanisms which could reduce the importance of the loss. In Chapter 6 we presented estimates of the numbers of grouse chicks killed by harriers, derived from data on provisioning rates at nests and numbers of harriers. We calculated the numbers of grouse chicks killed for the period up until the July brood counts and

Table 8.6 Estimates of grouse chick loss between the first week in June and the third week in July and the numbers of grouse chicks killed by harriers per 0.5 km² and as a percentage of June chick density

Per 0.5 km²	1993	1994	1995	1996
June chicks	22.9	31.6	30.7	24.8
July chicks	20.6±3.0	24.9±4.5	22.4±3.5	18.8±2.5
Chick loss to 17 July (%)	2.3 (10.1)	6.6 (21.0)	8.3 (27.0)	6.0 (24.4)
Chicks killed by harriers to 17 July (%)	3.1 (13.5)	11.1 (35.2)	11.2 (36.5)	9.7 (39.1)
Chicks killed by harriers to harrier dispersal (%)	4.3 (18.8)	14.2 (44.9)	13.6 (44.3)	14.0 (56.3)

also for the entire harrier breeding season until chick dispersal. Whilst it was possible to attach confidence limits to estimates of the numbers of chicks killed by harriers during some time periods, this was not possible in all periods in all years; neither was it possible to attach confidence limits to estimates of chicks killed per 0.5 km². We could compare these estimates of predation to measures of grouse chick loss derived from the June and July brood counts described in Chapter 7 (Table 8.6).

The data in Table 8.6 suggest that chick predation by harriers up until 17 July was greater than the observed chick losses between the June and July brood counts. We demonstrated in Chapter 7 that considerable brood reduction had already occurred by the time of the June brood counts. We recalculated chick loss for 1995 and 1996 using chick densities derived from the brood size of radio-tagged hens at hatch in the last week in May. These estimates of chick loss from May to July can be compared to estimates of harrier predation to 17 July (Table 8.7). Estimates of chick loss suggested that 43% (1995) and 47% (1996) of grouse chicks disappeared by 17 July. Harriers, however, were estimated to have killed by 17 July only 29% (1995) and 27% (1996) of the grouse chicks present at hatch. In other words, there were large unexplained early losses of grouse chicks which could not be attributed to harrier predation. Estimates of the total numbers of grouse chicks killed by harriers should also include predation during the period 17 July to harrier dispersal. Inclusion of harrier predation during this period suggested that 35% (1995) and 39% (1996) of the grouse chicks present at hatch at the end of May were killed by harriers up until harrier dispersal.

Compensation through unexplained loss of chicks

If these chicks had not been killed by harriers, were they likely to have died from other causes? Was there scope for compensation of these losses through other causes of chick mortality? The data presented in Table 8.7 suggest that unexplained losses of grouse chicks up until 17 July reduced chick densities by 14% in 1995 and 20% in 1996. Chick survival studies conducted at Langholm involving radio-tagged hens showed that most of these unexplained losses occurred during the first week after hatch. This finding from individual radio-tagged broods was supported by the observed reduction in size of randomly located broods found during the June brood counts (Chapter 7). L Parkinson *et al.* (unpublished data) found that chick survival during the first two weeks at Langholm was better in areas with boggy vegetation, and suggested that this may have been related to the abundance of invertebrates in such wet

Table 8.7 Estimates of grouse chick loss between the last week in May and the third week in July and the numbers of grouse chicks killed by harriers per 0.5 km² and as a percentage of May chick density

Per 0.5 km²	1995	1996
May chicks	39.1	35.7
July chicks	22.4±3.5	18.8±2.5
Observed chick loss to 17 July (%)	16.7 (42.7)	16.9 (47.4)
Chick killed by harriers to 17 July (%)	11.2 (28.6)	9.7 (27.2)
Unexplained chick loss to 17 July (%)	5.5 (14.1)	7.2 (20.2)
Chick killed by harriers to harrier dispersal (%)	13.6 (34.8)	14.0 (39.2)

areas. Other researchers have demonstrated that early mortality in red grouse and other gamebird chicks is common and often related to starvation (Savory 1977; Hudson 1986a; Bergerud 1988). Taken in total, these findings suggested that grouse at Langholm underwent considerable brood reduction, possibly due to starvation, prior to most of the harrier predation, and that predation may thus be largely additive to other causes of mortality. A further line of evidence suggesting that compensation through unexplained losses was unlikely was the lack of density dependence in chick survival.

The conclusion from Langholm that most grouse chick losses to harriers were additive to other causes of mortality was consistent with earlier findings involving comparison of grouse breeding success on moors with and without harriers (Redpath 1991). In this study, moors with breeding harriers produced an average 17% fewer young grouse than moors without breeding harriers. We can calculate an estimate of compensation of chick predation at Langholm assuming that the same proportion of the chicks killed by harriers would have disappeared from other causes, had they survived as in the chick population at large. As the unexplained chick losses to 17 July were 14% in 1995 and 20% in 1996, an average of 17% of the chicks killed by harriers to 17 July could have disappeared due to unknown causes had they not been killed by harriers. We do not believe that such a mechanism would occur after 17 July, and so have not included later chick losses in this calculation.

Were grouse broods during the study period smaller than earlier years?

If harrier predation of grouse chicks at Langholm was additive to other mortality, then grouse brood sizes should have been smaller on average during the study than before 1990 when harriers rarely bred successfully (Chapter 3). Transect counts of grouse were conducted by the Buccleuch Estate gamekeepers with their dogs during the last week in July from 1975 until the present. These counts assessed the relative abundance of grouse from year to year and were used as a guide to set the number of days of shooting in autumn (Chapter 10). Counts were conducted as line transects of approximately 3 km length, generally following the grouse drives used on shooting days. Grouse were classified as young

or old and totals were summed at the end of each transect. The same six areas were counted throughout and an average young/old ratio for each year was calculated.

The young/old ratios recorded by the gamekeepers during 1975–90 (median 3.2, quartiles 2.9–3.5) were significantly larger than those recorded by them during 1991–96 (median 2.3, quartiles 2.2–2.5) (Mann-Whitney Test U=91.5, n_1=16, n_2=6, P<0.001). The median values were thus 33% lower during the study than previously, which was again consistent with our own findings and with the view that raptor predation was additive. We also compared the young/old ratio recorded by the gamekeepers during 1992–96 to that recorded by ourselves during the same period (Chapter 7). Our estimates (median 2.1, quartiles 1.9–2.2) were slightly smaller than theirs (median 2.4, quartiles 2.3–2.5) (Wilcoxon Signed Ranks Test T=1, N=5, P=0.06).

Did summer raptor predation reduce autumn grouse density?

In the previous sections, we considered various compensatory mechanisms which could reduce the impact of the observed raptor predation on adult grouse and grouse chicks during summer at Langholm. We showed that virtually all female grouse at Langholm were territorial by April and that summer predation thus fell on territorial birds. Predatory mammals were rare and could compensate little of the raptor predation. Compensation through parasite-induced mortality or reduction in fecundity remains a possibility, but we do not know if and to what extent this could occur. It seemed that spring raptor predation at Langholm was largely additive and resulted in reductions in grouse breeding density of some 30%. In addition to this predation on adults, harriers killed on average 37% of the grouse chicks available at hatch by the time of harrier dispersal in early August. Most of these losses to predation occurred after the period of unexplained losses in the first week after hatch. As explained above, chick predation by harriers seemed largely additive and reduced chick survival by some 30%.

In Figure 8.2 we pull together these two aspects of summer predation to consider the potential impact of raptors on the numbers of grouse available for shooting in August. The

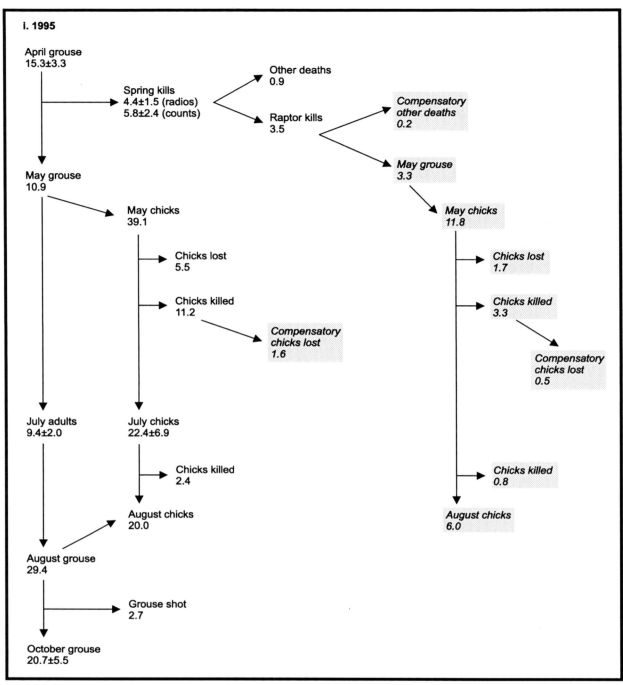

Figure 8.2i Flow chart of grouse population dynamics at Langholm during two summers. The numerical values are from 1995 when data collection was most complete. In both 1995 and 1996 figures are presented as means with 95% confidence limits where possible and in all cases are per 0.5 km². Italics denote what would have happened to grouse chicks had their parents not been killed by raptors and also possible mechanisms for compensation. Equal sex ratios are assumed throughout

numerical values in the Figure are based on 1995 and 1996 when raptor numbers were high and data collection was most complete. In both years values are presented as means with 95% confidence limits where possible, and in all cases denote birds per 0.5 km². Parts in italics denote what was likely to have happened to grouse chicks had their parents not been killed by raptors and also possible levels of compensation. Equal sex ratios are assumed throughout.

We start in April 1995 in the presence of raptors with observed densities of 15.3 grouse per 0.5 km² (Figure 8.2i). Our radio-tagging studies indicated that 4.4 grouse per 0.5 km² were killed during April and May, reducing adult densities at the end of May to 10.9 grouse per 0.5 km². It is important to stress here that similar estimates of early summer losses of grouse were derived independently from the grouse counts. Estimated grouse chick density at hatch in

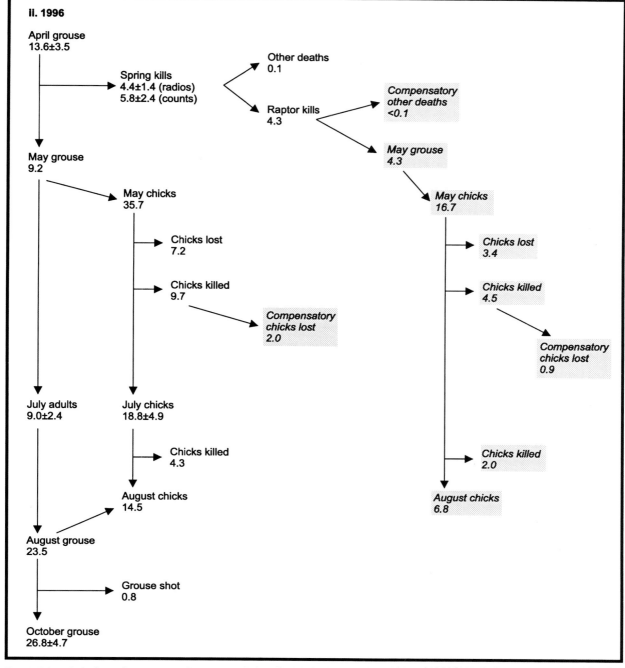

Figure 8.2ii Flow chart of grouse population dynamics at Langholm during two summers. The numerical values are from 1996 when data collection was most complete. In both 1995 and 1996 figures are presented as means with 95% confidence limits where possible and in all cases are per 0.5 km². Italics denote what would have happened to grouse chicks had their parents not been killed by raptors and also possible mechanisms for compensation. Equal sex ratios are assumed throughout

late May was 39.1 chicks per 0.5 km², of which 5.5 were lost to unknown causes and 11.2 were killed by harriers, giving an observed chick density in late July of 22.4 chicks per 0.5 km². A further 2.4 chicks per 0.5 km² were estimated to have been killed by harriers before harrier dispersal, leaving 20.0 chicks, which, when combined with the surviving adults, gave an estimate of August density in the presence of summer raptors of 29.4 grouse per 0.5 km². Shooting mortality reduced this figure by a

further 2.7 grouse per 0.5 km². The estimated post-shooting density (at 26.7 grouse per 0.5 km²) was greater than that observed in October (at 20.7 grouse per 0.5 km²), suggesting that further losses or net emigration occurred during the autumn prior to the October counts.

Estimation of August grouse densities in the absence of summer raptor predation must include losses as a result of chick predation by harriers and as a result of harrier and other raptor predation of adults in early summer. Predation of adults in early summer also resulted in the indirect loss of the chicks which they would have produced, and these figures were estimated on the assumption that the productivity of killed adults would have been similar to that of surviving adults. This estimate must also incorporate compensatory increases in other losses of both adults and chicks that could occur in the absence of raptors. The calculations for the 1995 summer are described in Figure 8.2i. August grouse densities in the absence of raptors can be estimated as:

Observed August grouse density with raptors	29.4	
Adults killed by raptors between April and May	+3.5	
Compensatory increase in other deaths of adults	−0.2	
Chicks killed by harriers between May and July	+11.2	'Direct loss'
Compensatory increase in unexplained losses of chicks	−1.6	
Chicks killed by harriers between July and August	+2.4	
Chicks killed by harriers between May and July	+3.3	
Compensatory increase in unexplained losses of chicks	−0.5	'Indirect loss' as a result of loss of adults in April and May
Chicks killed by harriers between July and August	+0.8	
Chicks which survive to August	+6.0	
August grouse density in absence of summer raptors	54.3	

The estimated August density in the absence of summer raptors was 54.3 grouse per 0.5 km², which, when compared with the estimated August density in the presence of summer raptors of 29.4 grouse per 0.5 km², suggested that raptor predation reduced August density in 1995 by 45%.
Approximately equal proportions of the lost productivity were due to predation of adult grouse by raptors in early summer and to predation of grouse chicks by harriers in mid-summer.

Similar calculations of estimated August grouse densities in the presence and absence of summer raptors were made for the 1996

summer (Figure 8.2ii). In 1996 a greater proportion of grouse chicks were estimated to have been killed by harriers after the July counts than in the previous summer, mainly as a result of a number of late harrier nests in that year. Overall, however, estimates of chick losses to harriers were similar between the two summers. August densities in 1996 in the presence of summer raptors were estimated at 23.5 grouse per 0.5 km², which, when subtracting shooting losses, suggested that net immigration on to our counting sites might have occurred before the October grouse counts. August densities in the absence of summer raptors could have been as high as 52.2 grouse per 0.5 km². Comparison with the observed densities suggests that predation by raptors in spring and summer reduced autumn densities in 1996 by some 55%.

Taken in total, the data presented in Figure 8.2 suggest that the levels of summer raptor predation at Langholm during 1995–96 reduced August grouse density within a single breeding season by approximately 50%. These figures are estimates and as such are subject to sampling and measurement errors. It is notable, however, that the estimates of adult grouse and grouse chick loss determined by radio-tracking and the harrier nest watches coincide closely with the estimates of loss determined from counts of grouse with dogs. The agreement in findings between these different methods gives us considerable confidence in their accuracy.

What was the long-term impact of summer raptor predation?
What effect was this summer predation likely to have had on subsequent grouse densities? We developed a simple model which used the estimated reduction in autumn grouse density caused by summer raptor predation, together with the observed patterns of density dependence in winter loss, to predict subsequent grouse densities in the absence of summer raptor predation. An assumption implicit in this model was that the observed density-dependent relationship for winter loss remained the same in the absence of summer raptor predation.

The model was applied in a very simple way assuming that the autumn grouse density (A) in year t was proportional to the previous spring density (S) as:

Equation 8.1
$$A_t = R_0 S_t$$

where R_0 is the reproductive rate which was calculated simply as autumn density divided by spring density. The observed autumn and spring densities and R_0 for each of the 'core' eight counting sites in the years 1993–96 are given in Table 8.8. R_0 in the presence of summer raptor predation was taken as the mean of these values, giving an estimate of 1.5 ± 0.07. R_0 in the absence of summer raptor predation can be estimated from the data presented in the previous section. These data suggested that, in the absence of raptors, autumn grouse densities would approximately double. R_0 in the absence of raptors was thus calculated by doubling the observed autumn densities in Table 8.8, giving a estimate of 3.0 ± 0.14. Clearly, a lower value of R_0 would be expected if shooting losses or dispersal were

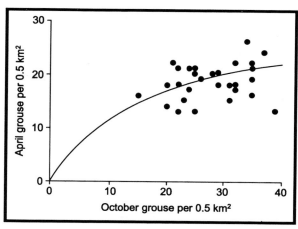

Figure 8.3 April grouse density at Langholm in relation to density the previous October for the restricted set of counting sites on the main part of Langholm moor. Non-linear relationship fit to model S=31 A (17+A)

density dependent. Furthermore, a lower value of R_0 would be expected if we had overestimated the impact of summer raptor predation.

In the model developed below there is a density-dependent relationship between spring density in year $t+1$ and autumn density in year t. The analysis of density dependence in winter loss was based on a linear relationship between log spring density and log autumn density which implied a power function. This is an unrealistic relationship for density dependence in territorial species because there is no ceiling on population size. Furthermore, it fails at low densities because the growth rate is unbounded. The power function is an empirical approximation which serves as a basis for detecting density dependence and predicting changes over a limited range of densities. We therefore considered a more realistic non-linear equation:

Equation 8.2
$$S_{t+1} = KA_t / (c + A_t)$$

where K is the carrying capacity of the moor which is assumed constant. We fitted the equation to the observed October and April grouse densities on the main part of the moor (excluding sites 5, 6, 11 & 12, see Chapter 7) by weighted least squares proportional to expected April density (Figure 8.3). This gave estimates of $K=31$ (SE=9) and $c=17$ (SE=13).

We now applied the model with the observed spring density in year t to predict the spring and autumn densities in years $t+1$ and $t+2$. As equation 8.2 was fitted to the data on grouse

Table 8.8 April and October grouse densities and estimates of reproductive rate (R_0) for the restricted set of eight counting sites at Langholm during 1993–96. Grouse densities are per 0.5 km² and R_0 is calculated as October density/April density

Year	1993	1994	1995	1996
April density				
LCF	18	18	17	16
LCL	13	21	18	15
LDH	16	20	20	20
LDL	15	22	21	19
LMB	21	22	17	14
LMM	21	17	13	13
LRF	19	30	18	18
LRR	26	30	24	22
October density				
LCF	29	32	15	29
LCL	22	20	23	22
LDH	29	25	28	27
LDL	32	25	26	36
LMB	21	32	20	24
LMM	24	22	25	36
LRF	36	31	32	30
LRR	40	37	35	29
R_0				
LCF	1.61	1.78	0.88	1.81
LCL	1.69	0.95	1.28	1.47
LDH	1.81	1.25	1.40	1.35
LDL	2.13	1.14	1.24	1.89
LMB	1.00	1.45	1.18	1.71
LMM	1.14	1.29	1.92	2.77
LRF	1.89	1.03	1.78	1.67
LRR	1.54	1.23	1.46	1.32

density from the main part of the moor only, we used as a starting point a spring density of 19 grouse per 0.5 km^2 which was the mean April density of those sites over the period of the study.

Monte Carlo simulation was used to estimate 95% confidence limits on the model predictions for the main part of the moor, based on the observed pattern of variation in R_0 and the mean residual sum of squares calculated from fitting equation 8.2. The year- and site-specific values of R_0 followed a log-normal distribution (ln-transformed values $\sim N(0.375, 0.255)$ with raptors, $N(1.069, 0.255)$ without raptors), while the SD of points around fitted equation 8.2 was 3.9. Each run involved simulating densities independently on eight 0.5 km^2 sites, then calculating the average, which was assumed to represent the whole of the main moor. On each site, a value of R_0 was generated from the relevant log-normal distribution and multiplied by S_t to produce A_t. If E_t was the result of applying equation 8.2 to A_t, then S_{t+1} was generated from the normal distribution $N(E_t, 3.9)$, and the cycle was repeated. The simulation was run 1000 times and the upper and lower 2.5th percentiles were taken as the 95% confidence limits.

Therefore, in the presence of summer raptor predation:

	95% CL
$S_t=19$	
$A_t = 1.5 \times 19 = 28.5$	(24–34)
$S_{t+1} = 31 \times 28.5/(17 + 28.5) = 19.4$	(16–22)
$A_{t+1} = 1.5 \times 19.4 = 29.1$	(23–36)
$S_{t+2} = 31 \times 29.1/(17 + 29.1 = 19.6$	(15–22)
$A_{t+2} = 1.5 \times 19.6 = 29.4$	(22–36)

and in the absence of summer raptor predation:

	95% CL
$S_t = 19$	
$A_t = 3.0 \times 19 = 57$	(47–68)
$S_{t+1} = 31 \times 57/(17 + 57) = 23.9$	(21–27)
$A_{t+1} = 3.0 \times 23.9 = 71.7$	(56–87)
$S_{t+2} = 31 \times 71.7/(17 + 71.7) = 25.1$	(22–28)
$A_{t+2} = 3.0 \times 25.1 = 75.3$	(59–94)

The model predicted that, with current levels of summer raptor predation, the spring and autumn grouse densities in years $t+1$ and $t+2$ remained similar to year t. This suggested that the Langholm grouse population was at equilibrium with current levels of mortality, production and movement of grouse, a result supported by the observed lack of variation in grouse density during the period of the study. In the absence of summer raptor predation, the model predicted that spring density in year $t+1$ would increase by 25%. Critically, however, the subsequent increase in spring density in year $t+2$ was only 5%. Similarly, the model predicted large increases in breeding production in the first two summers following removal of summer raptor predation, to a level 2.5 times that in the presence of raptors. By the third summer the increases had stabilised because of the observed density dependence in winter loss. The equilibrium levels with and without raptors were, respectively, 19.7 and 25.3 for spring density, and 29.5 and 76.0 for autumn density. It is unlikely that these maxima would be maintained in practice, because the model contained no delayed density dependence. The model was nevertheless robust for short-term predictions because from a stable population delayed density dependence could not become effective within two years.

In summary, the development of a simple model predicted that, in the absence of summer raptor predation, spring grouse densities would increase within two years to a level 1.3 times that in the presence of raptors. Similarly, the model predicted that breeding production in the absence of raptors would increase within two years to a level 2.5 times that in the presence of raptors. Despite considerable assumptions implicit in the model, it did show that increases of grouse in the absence of raptors were not boundless, and made quantitative predictions which would be amenable to testing by experiment.

Which raptors were responsible for summer predation?

Summer loss of grouse to raptors occurs in two ways:
- direct predation of chicks and adults
- indirect loss of chicks as a result of the deaths of their parents.

Earlier we estimated that 48% (1995) and 42% (1996) of the reduced summer production of grouse at Langholm was due to direct chick predation by harriers. The remaining losses were due either directly or indirectly to raptor predation of adults in early summer. In these two years we estimated that raptors killed 3.5 (1995) and 4.3 (1996) adult grouse per 0.5

km² in April and May. Which raptors were responsible for these adult deaths?

We were unable to distinguish between the kills of different species of raptors so we used the estimates of grouse killed by peregrines in Chapter 6 to try to answer this question. Estimates of peregrine kills of grouse during the breeding season based on biomass requirements indicated that peregrines killed 0.35–1.50 grouse per 0.5 km². This estimate only included breeding pairs and we had no information on the numbers of non-breeding peregrines. Clearly, however, breeding peregrines could not account for all the observed grouse mortality.

Female harriers may have killed adult grouse in early April before they started forming eggs, but we had no data on female diet at this time. Predation by female harriers in April should have been influenced by differences in the numbers of breeding birds and laying dates between years. In Chapter 6 we ranked the years of the study in order of decreasing numbers of female harrier days available for hunting in April as 1994, 1996, 1993, 1995 and 1992. If female harriers killed grouse in April, we would expect that ranking the years of the study in order of the extent of the summer loss of grouse would produce the same order. Ranking the years in this way as 1994, 1995, 1996 and 1993 (no data for 1992) provided little or no support for this hypothesis.

In 1995 and 1996, we investigated the survival of radio-tagged grouse in April and May in relation to their proximity to harrier and peregrine nests. We calculated the central point of each grouse home range as the average grid reference of all winter fixes. We measured the distance from this point to all harrier and peregrine nests and expressed this as the sum of the reciprocal squared for each species. There was no difference between grouse which lived or died in April and May in proximity to harrier or peregrine nests (1995 harrier t_{71}=0.55, P=0.58; 1995 peregrine t_{71}=0.97, P=0.35; 1996 harrier t_{51}=1.21, P=0.23; 1996 peregrine t_{51}=0.40, P=0.69).

In summary, harrier predation of grouse chicks caused 48% (1995) and 42% (1996) of the estimated reduction in grouse

productivity at Langholm. The remainder was due to losses caused by the death of adult grouse in early summer. However, we cannot reliably split these losses of adult grouse between harriers, peregrines or other raptors.

DISCUSSION
In this Chapter we considered the potential compensatory mechanisms which could reduce the impact of observed predation on the grouse population at Langholm. Our main conclusions were:
- we were unable to determine the extent to which winter predation was compensatory;
- the data were strongly suggestive that raptor predation in summer on adult grouse and chicks was largely additive and resulted in reductions in autumn density of 50% within a single breeding season;
- modelling predicted that, in the absence of summer raptors, grouse breeding density within two years would be 1.3 times greater, and breeding production 2.5 times greater, than in the presence of summer raptors.

Predators killed roughly 40% of the grouse population during the winter at Langholm. Such losses were also typical in other grouse populations, though not necessarily all due to predation. Radio-tagging suggested that predation during the second half of the winter was not restricted to non-territorial birds, and it appeared that territorial status did not determine overwinter survival, as documented in high-density grouse populations in NE Scotland (Watson 1985). Previous studies on low-density grouse populations in Strathspey also concluded that winter predation was not restricted to non-territorial birds (Hudson 1990, 1992). Given that both territorial and non-territorial grouse were killed by predators during the winter, one possible mechanism for compensation was that any territorial birds that died were replaced in the breeding population by non-territorial birds (Watson & Moss 1990). Winter compensation could thus occur through the movement of grouse. The extent of compensation would depend upon the relative timing of predation and movement, and our analysis indicated that this fell between 55% and 95%. Such analyses were conducted at the scale of the counting site, however, and compensation at the wider population scale through this mechanism would largely depend on the assumption that replacement birds were non-territorial and that non-territorial birds did not breed.

Compensation of winter raptor predation through the effects of parasites and mammalian predators remains a strong possibility. Previous work on the red grouse/ *T. tenuis* system has shown that parasites could reduce grouse survival and fecundity (Hudson 1986a, b, 1992; Hudson *et al.* 1992a, b). This work was conducted at high grouse density and less is known about the effects of parasites at lower intensities of infection and at lower densities of grouse. Worm burdens were low at Langholm during the course of the study but would almost certainly increase with grouse densities in the absence of raptors. What effect this would have on grouse productivity is currently unknown. Compensation of reduced winter raptor predation could occur to an extent through increased mammalian predation, but the strength of this compensation was limited because mammalian predators were controlled; this predation did not appear to be density dependent. However, the possibility remains that we did not detect density dependence in overwinter mammalian predation because our data were limited to four winters, or that the strength of the density dependence could change in the absence of raptors. In the light of all the above, it seems premature to draw firm conclusions regarding the impact of winter predation on subsequent breeding densities.

We estimated that summer raptor predation reduced grouse breeding densities by 30% and resulted in a 30% reduction in the numbers of chicks produced by the survivors, giving an overall reduction in August density of 50%. It seems unlikely that a significant amount of the summer raptor predation on adult grouse was compensatory. Few non-territorial grouse of either sex were alive by April and virtually all females attempted to breed. There thus seemed little scope for the late replacement of breeding females killed by raptors. Mammalian predation reduced grouse breeding density by only 3% and its effects were relatively trivial, probably because fox numbers were controlled. Compensation through parasitism remains a possibility but insufficient is known about the effects of parasites at low grouse densities.

Predation of adults could in theory be partially compensated through density-dependent chick survival, but there was no evidence for density dependence in chick survival at Langholm or in other grouse populations (Hudson 1986, 1992).

The 30% chick losses to predation were largely in addition to average unexplained losses of 17%, which occurred within the first two weeks after hatch. Studies on red grouse and other gamebirds suggested that much of this early chick mortality was due to starvation through invertebrate shortages (Savory 1977; Erikstad 1985; Hudson 1986; Potts 1986; Baines 1996), and preliminary work at Langholm on the relationship between chick survival and habitat use tended to support this view (L Parkinson *et al.,* unpublished data). Previous research indicated that annual variation in early chick survival could be partially explained by variation in egg quality, which in turn was determined by the condition of breeding females (Moss, Watson & Parr 1975; Moss *et al.* 1981). The occurrence of considerable brood reduction prior to most harrier predation, and the observed lack of density dependence in chick survival, suggested that harrier predation of chicks at Langholm was largely additive. Redpath (1991) similarly concluded that chick losses to harriers were additional to other losses from comparative studies on grouse moors in Perthshire and Strathspey.

Estimating the impact of raptors from April onwards involved combining direct predation of adult grouse and chicks with indirect losses of chicks caused by the deaths of their parents. In these calculations, it was necessary to remove those chicks that would have been lost to other causes and to incorporate some compensation from mammalian predation. Such estimates suggested that at Langholm raptors reduced the potential number of grouse available for shooting in August by around 50%. Approximately half of these losses were due to raptor predation of adult grouse in early summer. This estimate of impact assumed, from consideration of existing information, that most losses were additive. We had no data from places where harriers and peregrines had been removed, so the calculation of productivity in the absence of

8. Impact of predation

raptors remains hypothetical. Nevertheless, we now have a quantitative prediction which could be tested in field experiments.

Finally, we used a simple model to investigate the effect of summer raptor predation at Langholm on subsequent spring and autumn densities, incorporating the observed density dependence in winter loss. The model predicted that, in the absence of summer raptors, spring grouse densities would increase within two years to a level 1.3 times, and autumn grouse densities to a level 2.5 times, that observed in the presence of summer raptors. The model did not incorporate delayed density dependence and was therefore thought to be unrealistic for making predictions regarding equilibrium densities in the longer term. However, it did make a quantitative prediction that both spring and autumn densities would increase in the absence of summer raptor predation, which could again be tested by field experiment.

©Keith Brockie '97

Chapter 9

Red grouse chicks, 11 to 12 days old

9. Moorland habitat and grouse predation

- Winter losses of grouse from the Langholm study sites were lower on the sites with most heather. Our interpretation of this was that grouse moved into sites with more heather throughout the winter, partly compensating for local losses to predators.
- Summer losses of adult grouse on the same sites were also lower on sites with more heather and tall vegetation. We were unable to determine whether this was due to differential mortality or movement.
- The home ranges of radio-tagged grouse which survived the winter contained more bilberry than the home ranges of grouse which died, but no other differences in habitat were found between the two groups.
- We had no clear evidence that predation on adult grouse at Langholm was directly influenced by any of the measured habitat variables, or that vegetation influenced the success with which harriers caught their prey.
- Harriers attacked more grouse broods in areas with a mixture of heather and grass than expected from the proportion of grouse broods in that habitat.

INTRODUCTION

Many grouse at Langholm were killed by raptors (Chapter 7) and predation at recorded levels may have been sufficient to limit the grouse population at the densities observed (Chapter 8). Whilst predation was the proximate reason for the mortality, the ultimate reason may have lain elsewhere. In this Chapter, we explore the hypothesis that the present-day structure of the habitat may have influenced predation rates. The basic tenets of the argument are straightforward: heather cover has been lost from Langholm since 1948, probably as a result of sheep grazing (Chapter 2); the reduced heather cover meant that grouse were now more vulnerable to predation than they would have been if heather cover was good. Vulnerability could have been increased in two ways:

- through reduced heather quality making the grouse spend more time foraging and less time looking for predators;
- through reduced cover making grouse more visible or accessible to predators.

Furthermore, habitat could have influenced the movement patterns of grouse within a population, in response to the predation of other individuals.

This Chapter is split into three sections. In the first, we examine patterns of grouse losses, mortality and chick production on our study sites at Langholm, in order to assess whether the habitat within these sites could explain any of the observed demographic patterns. In the second section, we examine the habitat in the home ranges of radio-tagged birds to assess whether differences in habitat influenced the probability of a bird surviving or being killed by a raptor. In the last section, we examine harrier hunting success in different vegetation types, to see whether grouse may have been more detectable or accessible in certain habitats.

HABITAT AND GROUSE DEMOGRAPHY

The habitat characteristics of the counting sites could have influenced grouse on those sites in a number of ways.

- Habitat could have directly influenced territory size and thus the density of grouse.
- Habitat could have influenced predation rates of adult grouse, such that more grouse were killed on areas with certain characteristics.
- Habitat could have influenced the movement or dispersal patterns of grouse.
- Habitat could have influenced chick losses through increased susceptibility to either starvation or predation, as described above.

We used the data presented in Chapter 7 on grouse densities in October, April and

July and on the number of grouse found dead on each of our 0.5 km² counting sites. We surveyed the vegetation on each site, recording heather cover and the height and density of vegetation in 40 2 m x 2 m quadrats (Chapter 2).

Habitat and grouse density

We compared the measured density of grouse during October, April and July with measures of heather cover, vegetation height and vegetation density. In the statistical models, we used the average grouse density for each counting site during the years 1992–96, the log-transformed grouse density, measures of vegetation height, vegetation density and heather cover (arcsine-transformed). In each case, during October, April and July, the regression model that best explained grouse density included heather cover (Table 9.1): the more heather, the more grouse. Neither vegetation height nor vegetation density explained any significant variation in grouse density.

Habitat and winter loss

Winter losses on our study sites were density dependent (Chapter 7). Therefore, to investigate the effects of habitat on winter loss, we included October density in the statistical models. We entered April grouse density into a multiple regression model with October grouse density, heather cover and the height and density of the vegetation, having first transformed the variables as above. Having removed the effect of October grouse density, heather cover explained an additional 11.4% of the variation in April grouse density (Table 9.2). This analysis suggested that, October

Table 9.1 Results of multiple regression analyses on the relationship between grouse densities and habitat features

Variable	Regression coeff	r^2	T	F	P
October grouse density					
Constant	2.19	–	–	–	–
Heather cover (arcsin)	1.82	0.60	3.88	15.07	0.003
April grouse density					
Constant	1.54	–	–	–	–
Heather cover (arcsin)	2.19	0.66	4.44	19.70	0.001
July grouse density					
Constant	2.26	–	–	–	–
Heather cover (arcsin)	2.23	0.53	3.39	61.95	0.001

Table 9.2 Results of multiple regression analyses on the relationship between (i) winter loss of grouse and habitat features, and (ii) winter kills of grouse and habitat features

Variable	Regression coeff	r^2	T	P
i. Winter loss				
Constant	0.53	–	–	–
October grouse density (log)	0.48	0.62	5.38	<0.001
Heather cover (arcsin)	1.28	0.73	4.32	<0.001
ii. Winter kills				
Constant	–10.27	–	–	–
October grouse density (log)	6.76	0.43	5.83	<0.001

Significance of regression model (i) $F_{2,45}$=61.95, P<0.001, (ii) $F_{1,46}$=34.01, P<0.001

densities being equal, winter losses were lower on areas with more heather. But was this reduction due to differential predation or movement of grouse? We repeated the analysis with the number of winter kills found on each counting site as the dependent variable. After removing the effects of October grouse density, the habitat variables had no effect on the number of winter kills found (Table 9.2). It was not possible to test directly whether movement of grouse was influenced by the habitat variables because our measure of 'movement' incorporated October grouse density, and therefore was not statistically independent. However, as winter loss was determined by winter kills and unexplained changes in grouse density (assumed to represent net gain or loss of grouse due to movement), and winter kills were not apparently influenced by habitat, the most likely explanation was that grouse moved into areas with more heather, to some extent replacing birds removed by predators.

Habitat and summer loss

We conducted a similar analysis on the effect of the habitat on summer loss of adult grouse. We entered July adult grouse density into a multiple regression model with April grouse density and the habitat characteristics as explanatory variables. Data were transformed as above. Having removed the effect of April grouse density, the inclusion of heather cover and vegetation height into the regression model explained an additional 8.5% of the variation in July density (Table 9.3). Hence, grouse densities being equal, summer

Table 9.3 Results of multiple regression analyses on the relationship between (i) summer loss of grouse and habitat features, and (ii) grouse chick production and habitat features

Variable	Regression coeff	r^2	T	P
i. Summer loss				
Constant	2.08	–	–	–
April grouse density (log)	0.43	0.57	3.31	0.002
Heather cover (arcsin)	0.96	0.62	2.48	0.017
Vegetation height (log)	–0.50	0.66	–2.14	0.038
ii. Chick production				
Constant	1.30	–	–	–
July hen density (log)	1.10	0.82	14.48	<0.001

Significance of regression model (i) $F_{3,44}=27.95$, $P<0.001$, model, (ii) $F_{1,46}=212.43$, $P<0.001$

losses were lower on areas with more heather and with more tall vegetation. As we had no data on summer kills on our study sites, we could not distinguish between the effects of habitat on predation and on movement of grouse.

Habitat and grouse chick production

We adopted a similar approach to test for any effects of habitat on chick production, measured as the ratio of young birds/adult females on our counting sites in July. We have previously demonstrated that the young/hen ratio did not vary in relation to hen density (Chapter 7). We entered July chick density into a multiple regression model with July hen density and the habitat characteristics as explanatory variables. Data were transformed as above. The habitat variables had no obvious effect on the density of grouse chicks in July (Table 9.3).

HABITAT AND INDIVIDUAL SURVIVAL

We examined habitat in the home ranges of 162 grouse at Langholm. Home ranges were estimated from the central point of the fixes obtained from October to March, and vegetation was measured in 20 quadrats within 100 m of that point (Chapter 2). Of these birds, 82 died in the winter, whilst the rest survived beyond 31 March. We first conducted one-way analyses of variance on each of the variables individually, for survivors *versus* those that died (Table 9.4). These results suggested differences between the two types of bird in four of the variables: bilberry, grass, vegetation height and density. However, many of the variables were inter-correlated (Table 9.5). We then used logistic regression techniques to examine survival in relation to the measured vegetation characteristics (Table 9.6). These analyses were conducted separately for each vegetation variable and then together in a model that also included variables for year, site (based on the grouse beats at Langholm moor), sex and age (young or old) of the grouse. Of the measured habitat variables, only the cover of bilberry was found to have a significant effect on the probability of survival. Grouse with more bilberry in their home ranges had a greater probability of survival. However, with 17 independent variables, the chances of getting a significant result were high. There was no significant effect of heather cover, vegetation height or vegetation density.

In summary, slight differences were found between the home ranges of survivors and

Table 9.4 Comparisons of vegetation measures in home ranges of surviving and dying grouse, using one-way analyses of variance. Data represent mean values per home range, with the data from different years pooled

Variable	Survivors	Years pooled Non-survivors	F-value	P	1994–95	1995–96
Heather (*Calluna*)	50.9	53.1	1.19	0.3		
Heather (*Erica*)	2.2	1.9	1.58	0.2		*
Bilberry	3.6	2.1	9.38	0.003 **	+	***
Grass	36.6	32.9	3.91	0.05 *		*
Rushes	1.8	2.0	0.35	0.5		
Bracken	0.4	0.4	0.12	0.7		
Height	20.4	19.5	3.60	0.06 +		
Density 0–10	14.4	14.3	0.06	0.8		
Density 10–20	6.9	6.5	1.41	0.2		
Density 20–30	2.1	1.7	3.41	0.07 +		*
Density 30–40	0.4	0.3	0.90	0.3		+
Density 40–50	0.05	0.05	0.10	0.7		

+ P<0.1, * P<0.05, ** P<0.01. For winters 1994–95 and 1995–96, significance only is given. In these winters direction of difference was the same as in the overall data

Table 9.5 Correlation matrix of habitat variables measured in 162 home ranges

	Heather (*Calluna*)	Heather (*Erica*)	Bilberry	Grass	Rushes	Bracken	Height	Density 0–10	Density 10–20	Density 20–30	Density 30–40	Density 40–50
Heather (*Calluna*)	1.00											
Heather (*Erica*)	0.08	1.00										
Bilberry	−0.24	0.13	1.00									
Grass	−0.83	0.03	0.27	1.00								
Rushes	−0.21	−0.04	0.09	0.09	1.00							
Bracken	−0.21	−0.12	−0.03	0.11	0.14	1.00						
Height	0.16	0.19	0.11	0.05	0.25	0.29	1.00					
Density 0–10	0.42	−0.03	0.04	−0.07	−0.04	−0.05	0.65	1.00				
Density 10–20	0.35	0.12	0.03	−0.17	0.01	0.08	0.84	0.66	1.00			
Density 20–30	0.33	0.17	0.02	−0.24	−0.03	0.09	0.73	0.35	0.83	1.00		
Density 30–40	0.34	0.11	−0.05	−0.30	−0.07	0.05	0.49	0.17	0.55	0.85	1.00	
Density 40–50	0.24	0.16	−0.09	−0.20	−0.08	−0.02	0.33	0.13	0.38	0.61	0.82	1.00

Critical values: $P<0.05$, $r=0.15$, $P<0.01$, $r=0.2$. Significant values are underlined

non-survivors. Surviving birds tended to live in areas with more bilberry, though whether this was a statistical anomaly or reflected real differences in the home ranges of surviving grouse was uncertain.

HABITAT AND RAPTOR HUNTING

During the five years at Langholm, we observed 198 strikes by adult harriers at prey, of which 31% resulted in capture. These strikes were classified into four main habitat types:

- burnt and young heather,
- building and mature heather,
- heather/grass mixture,
- grass/rushes.

The percentage of successful strikes differed between these four categories (Table 9.7), but not significantly so (all data G=6.7, 3 df, NS). In addition to estimating vegetation category, we also estimated the height of the vegetation at the strike site (Table 9.7). Again, differences were not significant (all data

G=0.3, 3 df, NS). At Langholm, therefore, while harriers appeared to be slightly more successful at catching prey in heather/grass mixtures, there was no clear evidence that vegetation category or height influenced their success.

At Langholm we observed 31 interactions between harriers and grouse broods, of which ten resulted in a capture. We combined these data with those previously collected by Redpath (1989), and again found no effect of vegetation category on hunting success (Table 9.8). We finally compared success in relation to two vegetation heights (<20 cm and >20 cm). While harriers appeared more successful at catching grouse chicks in short vegetation, the differences were not significant. In other words, once a grouse brood had been detected, the probability of a successful capture did not seem to be influenced by any of the measured vegetation characteristics.

Table 9.6 Results of logistic regression analysis of adult grouse survival in winter in relation to vegetation characteristics in their home ranges. The analysis was conducted separately for the vegetation measures individually and then together with variables for area, age, sex and year. Figures show estimates of regression coefficients, standard errors, t-ratio, significance and R^2 in single models and t-ratio and significance in full model

Variable	Estimate	SE	t	P	R^2(%)	t	P
Heather (*Calluna*)	−0.008	0.007	−1.09	NS	0.5	0.92	NS
Heather (*Erica*)	0.082	0.065	1.26	NS	0.8	0.31	NS
Bilberry	0.122	0.043	2.76	<0.01	5.0	2.89	<0.01
Grass	0.015	0.008	1.95	NS	1.8	1.18	NS
Rushes	−0.026	0.044	−0.59	NS	0.2	−1.41	NS
Bracken	0.038	0.101	0.37	NS	0.1	−0.90	NS
Height	0.057	0.030	1.87	NS	1.6	1.50	NS
Density 0–10	0.013	0.054	0.25	NS	0.1	−1.46	NS
Density 10–20	0.052	0.043	1.19	NS	0.6	−0.80	NS
Density 20–30	0.134	0.074	1.81	NS	1.6	1.08	NS

Table 9.7 The number and percentage success of strikes at prey by adult harriers at Langholm, classified by four habitat types and by vegetation height. Data are presented for all harrier strikes, summer (May–September) strikes and interactions with grouse broods. Latter data are combined with observations from previous work (Redpath 1989)

| | All strikes | | Summer strikes | | Grouse interactions | |
	Number	% successful	Number	% successful	Number	% successful
Habitat						
Burnt/young heather	10	40	6	33	17	47
Mature heather	107	35	44	27	30	30
Heather grass	46	50	20	50	23	43
Grass/rushes	38	24	30	20	3	33
G-statistic	6.58 NS		5.08 NS		1.73 NS	
Height						
<10 cm	19	42	13	39		
10–20 cm	30	37	17	35	19	47
20–30 cm	99	35	38	21		
30+ cm	34	38	19	42	48	30
G-statistic	0.35 NS		3.40 NS		1.13 NS	

Critical value for G-test (3 df) at P<0.05=7.81

Habitat may have influenced detection rates of grouse broods, such that broods in certain habitats were more readily detected by harriers than those in other habitats. To test for this influence, we compared the distribution of broods in early June in the four basic habitat categories at Langholm with the distribution of interactions between harriers and grouse broods in those habitats (Table 9.12). The majority (90%) of interactions were observed in two of the six grouse beats, so we used only data collected within these areas. We used the tests for selection outlined in Manly, McDonald and Thomas (1993), section 4.6. Such tests suggested that broods in certain habitats were more readily detected than others (X_L^2=49.3, 3 df, P<0.001). The significance of this result should be treated with caution, however, because two of the expected values were less than five. The application of 95% Bonferroni confidence limits indicated that broods in a mixture of heather and grass were more likely to be detected than expected from their distribution. In this habitat type, only 6% of broods were located, but 36% of observed interactions occurred there. This may have been a result of increased brood visibility to harriers, or a result of harriers selectively hunting this habitat. We have no data on fine-scale habitat use by harriers at Langholm, so can say nothing about the mechanisms behind this pattern of increased detection.

DISCUSSION

We were unable to find any evidence that predation on adult grouse was directly influenced by the measured habitat variables. However, our data did indicate that habitat may have been an important factor influencing the dynamics of the grouse population at Langholm. Grouse densities were highest on sites with the most heather, and the amount of heather cover had a positive effect on the persistence of grouse in our counting sites, the highest losses occurring on areas with the least heather cover. In winter, this did not appear to be due to higher predation levels in sites with least heather, as the numbers of kills found were not related to habitat, but the pattern was probably due to movement into the heather-dominated areas. That predation in winter was not directly influenced by

Table 9.8 The proportions of grouse broods and interactions between harriers and grouse broods in four vegetation types at Langholm during 1993–96. Data are from the two grouse beats where 90% of all interactions were observed. Confidence limits are derived using equation 4.13 in Manly et al. (1993)

Habitats	Young /burnt heather	Mature heather	Heather/ grass mix	Grass
Broods (N=65)	0.23	0.65	0.06	0.015
Interactions (N=28)	0.11	0.50	0.36	0.036
95% confidence limits	0.00–0.26	0.26–0.74	0.13–0.59	0.00–0.12

habitat was supported by the lack of clear differences in the home range habitat of those grouse that survived the winter and those that died. What differences there were between the home ranges of survivors and non-survivors suggested that those grouse which survived had more bilberry in their home ranges. This could be a result of density-dependent predation, with more grouse being killed on the high-density areas, while those on the lower-density areas where there was more bilberry survived.

Although the density of adult grouse was higher on sites with more heather, there was no evidence that breeding performance varied in relation to any of the measured habitat variables within the study sites. Thus, females on sites with little heather and low grouse density produced as many offspring as females on sites with more heather and higher grouse densities.

To judge from strike success, harriers tended to be slightly more successful at catching prey in a mixture of heather and grass than in the other habitat categories, though the differences were not significant. When interactions with grouse chicks were considered, there was evidence that grouse broods were more likely to be detected in a mixture of heather and grass than expected from the distribution of grouse broods. We were unable to say whether this was due to habitat selection by hunting harriers or the increased detectability of broods in that habitat. Vegetation type or height had no apparent influence on the chance of a capture of a grouse chick, once a brood had been detected. However, these findings need caution because habitat type and height were assessed from an observation point, not at the actual strike site. In some heterogeneous habitats, a harrier may appear to be in tall vegetation, whereas the vegetation at the actual strike site may be short. This was considered less of a problem in continuous heather stands.

In conclusion, we gained no evidence that predation on adult grouse was directly influenced by heather cover or other habitat variables. Habitat may have had a small and more subtle influence on grouse populations, causing birds to move into heather areas and out of grassy areas. Also, in summer, broods in a mixture of heather and grass were probably more likely to be detected by harriers than broods in other habitats.

Chapter 10

Headkeeper, Brian Mitchell, driving grouse with beaters

10. Bag records

- Grouse bags on the Eskdale part of Langholm moor declined significantly during 1913-90. The 1950–90 grouse bags from all of Langholm moor also showed a similar downward decline.
- Autocorrelation analysis of the Langholm grouse bags during the period 1950–90 indicated a tendency to fluctuate with a periodicity of six years.
- The six-year period of successive decline in grouse bags following the 1990 peak was three times longer than any decline since the second world war, and on the Eskdale part of the moor, the longest since records began in 1913.
- A model based on Langholm grouse bags from 1950–90 showed that the observed bags during 1995 and 1996 were significantly lower than expected and continued to decline, while the model predicted an increase.
- Comparison of grouse bags from Langholm with two nearby moors showed that bags on all three moors tended to fluctuate in synchrony during 1975–90. Since 1993, while the Langholm bags were still declining, those on the nearby moors rose. The most obvious difference between these moors after 1993 was that Langholm had high densities of harriers and peregrines, whilst the other moors had low densities of these raptors.
- Models based on the bags from the nearby moors during 1975–90 showed that the observed bags at Langholm were significantly lower that expected during 1995 and 1996.
- Shortfalls in bags from predicted values increased with the numbers of breeding raptors on the moor.
- There was no firm evidence of undershooting at Langholm during 1993–96.

INTRODUCTION

Upland sporting estates in Britain keep detailed records of the number of grouse shot in each year and for many estates these records stretch back to the 19th century. Several authors have analysed grouse bags from various regions of Britain, paying particular attention to the occurrence of population cycles, together with long-term trends and geographical variation in bags (Middleton 1934; Mackenzie 1952; Potts, Tapper & Hudson 1984; Williams 1985; Barnes 1987; Hudson 1992). It is important to distinguish between short-term and long-term variation in grouse bags. Short-term cyclic fluctuations of four to ten years oscillate around a mean, with peaks at regular intervals, whilst long-term trends refer to changes in this mean value.

In this Chapter, we first investigate long-term trends in the numbers of grouse shot at Langholm up until 1990, just before the start of our study in 1992. We then test for the presence of short-term cyclic fluctuations. Finally, we analyse in more detail the decline in the numbers of grouse shot at Langholm since 1990 and examine whether this decline was more prolonged than expected from past

bag records at Langholm and from other nearby grouse moors. In all of these analyses we distinguished between events in 1950–90 and in 1991–96. It was during the latter period that attempts were made to protect raptors at Langholm (although the eggs were taken from the two harrier nests in 1992) and when the current study was undertaken. According to the local Raptor Study Group, harriers attempted to breed in low numbers each year during 1986–90, but breeding success was generally poor (see Figure 3.1).

LONG-TERM TRENDS

Whilst it is known that record bags were shot at Langholm prior to the first world war (eg 29 092 in 1911 including 2523 grouse in one day on Roan Fell (Hamilton 1922)), continuous runs of bag records are available only for more recent years. For management purposes, the Buccleuch Estates have traditionally split the moor in two – Eskdale and Liddesdale. Bag records for Eskdale were available for 1913–96 and for Liddesdale for 1933–96, and we combined them to produce a single figure for grouse bags on the whole of Langholm moor for 1933–96 (Figure 10.1).

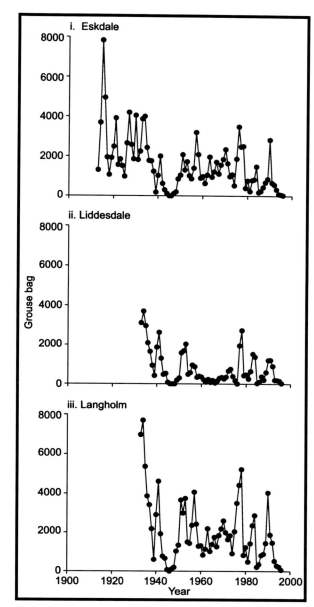

Figure 10.1 The numbers of red grouse shot on (i) the Eskdale part of Langholm moor during 1913–96; (ii) the Liddesdale part of Langholm moor during 1933–96; and (iii) the combined Langholm moors during 1933–96

Table 10.1 Results of fitting a linear long-term trend to log grouse bags on the Eskdale part of Langholm moor during 1913–90, first ignoring autocorrelation and then assuming first- and second-order autoregressive models of the residual variation. Bags during the years 1939–48 were excluded from the analysis. Note that the P-values are two-tailed and need to be divided by two for a one-tailed test

Method	b (SE)	t	P
Ordinary least squares	−0.017 (0.003)	−5.54	<0.001
AR (1) residual	−0.017 (0.004)	−3.57	<0.001
AR (2) residual	−0.016 (0.004)	−4.15	<0.001

based on ordinary linear regression are likely to be biased. We therefore tested for a long-term trend during 1913–90 by fitting a straight line to the log-transformed bag by ordinary least squares ignoring autocorrelation, and then by allowing for autocorrelation by assuming first- and second-order autoregressive models for the residual random variation (Table 10.1). The estimated slopes were virtually identical in each case, but the standard errors were larger in the analyses which allowed for autocorrelation. The evidence for a downward trend in bags was strong, irrespective of which model was used for the random component. The linear decline of −0.017 in the log bag corresponds to an approximate 1.7% per annum decline in the bag.

We repeated this analysis using the 1950–90 bag records for all Langholm moor combined, and tested the trend (Table 10.2). The linear decline of −0.013 in the log bag which corresponded to an approximate 1.3% per annum decline in the bag was slightly less than (but not significantly) that for the full period for Eskdale alone (1913–90).

We also examined the Eskdale series for evidence of a change in the rate of decline before and after 1950. The slopes for the model fitted to the data for the two periods 1913–38 and 1950–90 were −0.006 (SE±0.013)

We initially used the 1913–90 bag records for the Eskdale part of the moor to investigate long-term trends in the numbers of grouse shot there up until the start of our study. Visual examination suggests that the Eskdale grouse bags fluctuated around a higher mean level during the period prior to the second world war (pre-1940) than during the period after the second world war (post-1950). There appears to have been little shooting during and immediately after the war, and we therefore excluded bags from 1939–48 in the test for trend. For time series data, such as grouse bags, where there is likely to be autocorrelation between successive observations, tests for trends in the series

Table 10.2 Results of fitting a linear long-term trend to log grouse bags at Langholm moor during 1950–90, first ignoring autocorrelation and then assuming first- and second-order autoregressive models of the residual variation. Note that the P-values are two-tailed and need to be divided by two for a one-tailed test

Method	b (SE)	t	P
Ordinary least squares	−0.014 (0.008)	−1.76	0.09
AR (1) residual	−0.007 (0.006)	−1.07	0.24
AR (2) residual	−0.007 (0.005)	−1.37	0.17

and −0.017 (SE±0.012). However, these rates were not significantly different from one another, and neither was significantly different from zero. The latter result was probably a consequence of the loss of statistical power resulting from splitting the count series.

In summary, analysis of bag records for the Eskdale half of Langholm moor indicated that the numbers of grouse shot declined significantly during the period 1913–90. Similar analysis of the bags for all Langholm combined and for Eskdale alone during the shorter period 1950–90 indicated similar but less marked downward trends in numbers of grouse shot; these differences were not statistically significant. Neither was the decline significantly different from zero.

SHORT-TERM FLUCTUATIONS
The statistical method used to test for the presence of cycles in time series data, such as grouse bags, is called autocorrelation analysis (Royama 1992). This method correlates the number of grouse shot in each year with the number shot in each succeeding year at increasing time intervals or lags. In a cyclic time series, high correlations occur when the intervals in years match corresponding phases of the cycle.

We used the grouse bag records for all Langholm combined for the period 1950–90. The bag data were transformed to natural logarithms before analysis because population changes are multiplicative. The Langholm series of bags produced negative autocorrelations at time lags of three and nine years and positive autocorrelations at time lags of six years (Figure 10.2). In other words, the Langholm grouse bags showed a tendency to fluctuate with a periodicity of six years. Prior to the start of our study, there were obvious peaks in grouse bags at Langholm in 1978, 1984 and 1990. It is worth noting that a regular period of six years is a property of the autocorrelation function rather than the series itself, for which there is irregularity and variation in times between observed peaks. Autocorrelation analysis requires stationary data with no long-term trends in mean or variance, but a similar pattern of autocorrelation was obtained using detrended data (section below).

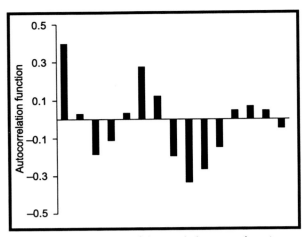

Figure 10.2 Correlograms of the Langholm grouse bags in 1950–90 plotting autocorrelation coefficients with increasing time lags up to 15 years

POST-1990 DECLINE
The current grouse management regime was established at Langholm in 1975 with the appointment of the present head-gamekeeper. The grouse bags have gone through three major cycles during the period 1975–present. The last peak, in which 4038 birds were shot, was in 1990. Grouse bags have declined in successive years to 67 in 1996. We have adopted a number of approaches to assess whether or not the recent decline was unusually long and whether fewer grouse were shot during the period of the study than could be expected.

Was the post-1990 decline longer than expected?
The first and simplest approach is to consider the number of years in which the Langholm grouse bag has successively declined since 1990 in relation to the duration of previous declines. For the post-war period 1950–96, peaks in the bags were observed in 1951, 1953, 1957, 1960, 1963, 1966, 1970, 1973, 1978, 1980, 1984 and 1990 (Figure 10.1). A peak is defined here as a year in which more grouse were shot than in the previous year and in the following year, regardless of the magnitude of the difference. There were therefore more 'peaks' for this analysis than the more regular major peaks identified by the autocorrelation analysis. The lengths of the decline phases following the above peaks were 1, 2, 2, 1, 1, 1, 2, 1, 1, 1, 1, and then 6 years of successive decline following the 1990 peak. In other words, the current decline phase was three times longer than any other decline phase observed since 1950.

We repeated the above analysis with the longer series of bag records for the Eskdale part of Langholm moor. For the period 1913–96, peaks in the Eskdale bags were observed in 1915, 1921, 1923, 1927, 1930, 1934, 1941, 1951, 1953, 1957, 1960, 1966, 1970, 1973, 1976, 1978, 1980, 1984 and 1990 (Figure 10.1). The lengths of the decline phases following the above peaks were 3, 1, 2, 2, 1, 5, 5, 1, 2, 2, 1, 1, 2, 1, 1, 1, 1, 1, and 6 years of decline following the 1990 peak. The probability of observing a value as extreme as the last one is thus 1/20=0.05. Two decline phases of comparable length to the present one were observed immediately before and during the second world war. Grouse bags declined for five successive years from 1934 to 1939, and again from 1941 to 1946. In this latter case, bags remained very low until 1949 and reflected national trends of limited grouse shooting and low bags during the war years (Barnes 1987; Hudson 1992).

In summary, the 1990–96 decline in grouse bags on Langholm moor lasted three times longer than any decline since 1950, and on the Eskdale part of the moor was the longest since records began in 1913.

Were the 1991–96 bags lower than expected from previous bags?

During 1975–90, grouse bags at Langholm showed a fairly regular six-year cycle, with peaks in 1978 (5234), 1984 (2860) and 1990 (4038). Crude estimates of the bags expected in the period 1991–96 could be calculated as the average bags from equivalent stages of the previous three cycles. For 1991–96 these estimated bags were 956, 832, 113, 1941, 2744 and 4044 respectively. Observed bags for these years were 1879, 1473, 523, 284, 221 and 67. The last three values were an order of magnitude lower than the equivalent values in the three previous cycles.

The total bags for 1991–96 were 4447 grouse compared with an average of 10 603 grouse in the previous two cycles, a 58% reduction. Remember that this last cycle included two years before the start of our study.

To examine the statistical significance of these lower bags, we needed to allow for

Table 10.3 Estimated parameters in time series model fitted to log grouse bags at Langholm during 1950–90. Model: long-term cubic time trend with coefficients (b_1, b_2, b_3) + second-order autoregressive scheme for residuals (a_1, a_2). Estimated standard deviation of random component=0.62

Parameter	Estimate (SE)
b_1	−0.179 (0.534)
b_2	−0.066 (0.398)
b_3	−0.180 (0.802)
a_1	0.405 (0.179)
a_2	−0.229 (0.183)

annual variability and autocorrelation, as well as for the possibility of long-term temporal trends in bags. Our approach was to use a simple dynamic population model. Two current hypotheses for grouse cycles implicate parasites and/or kin selection (Hudson et al. 1992; Moss et al. 1996). In both situations we expect grouse densities in year t to be related to grouse densities in year $t–1$ and $t–2$. The simplest empirical model is a second-order autoregressive scheme given by:

Equation 10.1
$$X_t - m = a_1 (X_{t-1} - m) + a_2 (X_{t-2} - m) + Z_t$$

where X_t denotes log density in year t and m is the mean log density. Z_t is a random term representing a perturbation due to exogeneous environmental variation. The model can produce quasi-cycles with length determined by the autoregression coefficients a_1 and a_2. In the above formulation the mean population density is constant but we can allow the mean to vary systematically with time as:

Equation 10.2
$$X_t - m_t = a_1 (X_{t-1} - m_{t-1}) + a_2 (X_{t-2} - m_{t-2}) + Z_t$$

Applying the model to log bag data assumes that the bag is proportional to the density. However, there is also likely to be a

Table 10.4 Predicted values of log grouse bags at Langholm based on the model described in Table 10.3

Year	Observed	Predicted	95% lower	95% upper
1991	7.54	7.42	6.17	8.68
1992	7.30	6.79	5.44	8.15
1993	6.26	6.70	5.34	8.05
1994	5.65	6.76	5.39	8.12
1995	5.39	6.76	5.39	8.12
1996	4.21	6.69	5.32	8.06

component of random variation in the bag akin to random measurement error.

The autoregressive model was fitted to the 1950–90 Langholm grouse bag data, assuming for the long-term trend a cubic function for the mean ($m_t = b_0 + b_1t + b_2t^2 + b_3t^3$). This allowed for the possibility that the low bags during 1993–96 were the continuation of a long-term decline. Table 10.3 gives estimates of the parameters in the fitted model. Although the effect of delayed density dependence was not statistically significant, it is included because of more general considerations and knowledge of cycles in grouse populations.

Table 10.4 shows the model predictions for log bags during 1991–96 starting with the observed bags in 1989 and 1990. The values show a rapidly damped oscillation about the declining trend in the mean. This is because the cyclical signal in the fitted model is rather weak and a large part of the variation in the time series has been ascribed to the random component. The fitted model peaks again in 1995, some five years on from the previous peak in 1990. Rapid damping of the fitted model severely limits its use for making predictions about bags in particular years. However, the confidence limits on the predictions are useful in revealing anomalies in the observed bags during 1991–96. The observed log bags for 1993–94 are within the estimated 95% confidence limits, but the values for 1995–96 both fall below the lower 95% limit. Note also that all observed values for 1993–96 are lower than the predicted values. More realistic predictions of bags in each of the years 1991–96 are presented below, based on the relationship between bags at Langholm and nearby moors.

We applied the same autoregressive model to the keepers' counts for 1975–90. These also showed a tendency to fluctuate with a periodicity of six years (Figure 10.5). The observed counts for 1995 and 1996 were below the lower 95% confidence limit calculated using the model, thus providing evidence of lower grouse numbers than expected, and not just lower bags. In each of the six years 1991–96, observed (and expected) values were as follows: 38 (67),

Table 10.5 Nesting attempts and breeding success of hen harriers and peregrines on moors F and G during 1993–96. Data were provided by RSPB

| Year | Nesting attempts of harriers | | Successful nests | | | |
| | | | of harriers | | of peregrines | |
	F	G	F	G	F	G
1993	2	1	0	0	3	1
1994	1	1	0	1	3	1
1995	2	2	0	1	3	1
1996	2	2	0	2	3	1

30 (51), 27 (47), 31 (51), 20 (56) and 17 (58), so by 1996 the keepers' count was about 30% of the predicted value.

To summarise, the autoregressive model for the Langholm bags during 1950–90 demonstrated that bags during 1995 and 1996 were significantly lower than expected.

Were the 1991–96 Langholm bags lower than those predicted from bags on nearby grouse moors?

Grouse bag records were also available from moor F and moor G, approximately 30 km from Langholm. Moor F was approximately the same size as Langholm with an estimated 3600 ha of heather ground, whereas moor G was smaller with an estimated 2400 ha of heather. The two moors shared a common boundary and were adjacent to two other moors for which grouse bag records were not available.

Information on harrier and peregrine breeding attempts on moors F and G during 1993–96 were provided by the RSPB (Table 10.5). In each of these years, harriers attempted to breed on both moors but these attempts, particularly on moor F, were rarely successful. The reasons for these breeding failures were unknown, but illegal control was suspected by the RSPB. Taking into consideration the combined size of moors F and G, and the average number of nests in each year 1993–96, harriers attempted to breed at mean densities of one female per 1850 ha of heather ground. The comparable average density of harrier breeding attempts at Langholm over the same time period was about four times as great, at one female per 430 ha. Harrier breeding success on moors F and G was generally poor, and the average density of successful females during 1993–96 was one per 6000 ha. In contrast, harrier

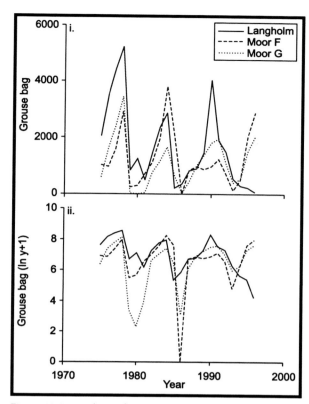

Figure 10.3 Numbers of red grouse shot on Langholm moor during 1975–96 in comparison with numbers shot on nearby moors F and G during the same period. Data are on linear scale (i) and log scale (ii)

Table 10.6 Predicted log bags at Langholm during 1991–96 from bags at moor G, using linear regression between log bags during 1975–90

Year	Observed bags	Predicted bags	95% lower	95% upper
1991	7.54	7.68	6.09	9.28
1992	7.30	7.53	5.82	9.24
1993	6.26	7.22	5.52	8.92
1994	5.65	7.30	5.60	9.00
1995	5.39	7.63	5.91	9.35
1996	4.21	7.73	5.99	9.46

Test for lower bags during 1991–96, $t_{18}=-3.15$, $P<0.001$

breeding success at Langholm was generally good over the same time period and the average density of successful females was one per 500 ha. Three peregrine pairs bred successfully on moor F and one on moor G throughout this period, giving a combined density of one eyrie per 1500 ha of heather. Comparable densities of breeding peregrines at Langholm over this time period were about twice as great, at one eyrie per 800 ha of heather. In summary, harriers at Langholm attempted to breed at four times the density, and successfully bred at ten times the density, of harriers on moors F and G. Peregrines at Langholm bred at twice the density as on moors F and G.

Comparison of grouse bags from the three moors during the period 1975–90 suggested that bags at Langholm cycled in synchrony with those on the nearby moors (Figure 10.3), with peak bags in 1978, 1984 and 1990 or 1991. Langholm bags were more closely related to bags at moor G than to those at moor F (Langholm and moor G: r=0.62, N=19, P<0.01; Langholm and moor F: r=0.34, N=18, P=0.22). Grouse bags on

all three moors declined following the peak in 1990 or 1991. Grouse bags on moors G and F increased in 1994 and had risen to 2016 on moor G and 2868 on moor F by 1996. Grouse bags at Langholm continued declining during this time. Evidently the relatively low density of breeding raptors on moors F and G did not prevent the grouse bags from increasing to levels comparable to earlier peaks.

Predictions of bags at Langholm were made separately on the basis of bags at moors G and F from a linear regression relating log bags on the different moors during 1975–90 (Tables 10.6 & 10.7). Records from both moors predicted a decline at Langholm from 1990 to 1993 followed by an increase to 1996. In both cases, the observed Langholm bags in 1995 and 1996 were below the lower 95% confidence limit on predicted levels. Predictions of grouse bags at Langholm for 1991–96, based on bags at moors G and F during this period, retained their amplitude of fluctuation. They therefore provided more realistic estimates for individual years than those based on an autoregressive model. On this basis, the average predicted figures for Langholm

Table 10.7 Predicted log bags at Langholm during 1991–96 from bags at moor F, using linear regression between log bags during 1975–90

Year	Observed bags	Predicted bags	95% lower	95% upper
1991	7.54	7.40	5.44	9.36
1992	7.30	7.18	5.20	9.16
1993	6.26	6.46	4.01	8.91
1994	5.65	7.03	5.00	9.06
1995	5.39	7.60	5.60	9.61
1996	4.21	7.75	5.67	9.82

Test for lower bags during 1991–96, $t_{18}=-2.55$, $P<0.01$

Table 10.8 Observed grouse bag as a percentage of predicted grouse bag compared to the numbers of harriers and peregrines breeding at Langholm during 1991–96. Predicted grouse bags are derived from the autoregressive model of the Langholm grouse bags in 1950–90 and linear regressions between the Langholm bags during 1975–90 and bags from moors G and F. Log bags have been back-transformed to the linear scale for ease of comparison

Year	Observed bag	Observed bag as % of predicted bag			Attempted breeding		Successful breeding	
		L	G	F	Harrier	Peregrine	Harrier	Peregrine
1991	1879	113	86	115	3	3	2	3
1992	1473	150	79	112	2	3	0	1
1993	523	64	38	82	5	3	4	1
1994	284	33	19	25	11	6	8	3
1995	221	26	11	11	8	6	8	3
1996	67	8	3	3	14	5	12	5

during 1991–96 from moors G and F together were 1900, 1588, 1003, 1304, 2028 and 2299 respectively. These figures compared with observed bags of 1879, 1473, 523, 284, 221 and 67.

In summary, comparison of grouse bags from Langholm with those from two nearby moors where harrier breeding densities and breeding success were low showed that the bags on all three moors tended to fluctuate

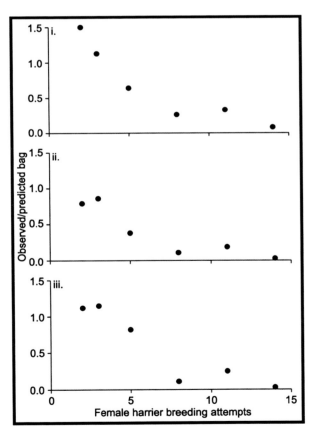

Figure 10.4 Observed bags expressed as a proportion of predicted bags in relation to the number of female harrier breeding attempts during 1991–96. Predicted bags are based on the autoregressive model of Langholm bags in 1950–90 (i) and the linear regressions between the Langholm bags during 1975–90 and bags from moor G (ii) and moor F (iii)

together during 1975–93. After 1993 the Langholm bags continued to decline whilst those on the nearby moors rose to high levels. Predictions of the Langholm bags during 1991–96 using bags on the nearby moors during 1975–90 indicated that the Langholm bags were significantly lower than expected in 1995 and 1996.

Low bags in relation to raptor densities
For predicted bags based on both methods, we calculated the observed bag as a percentage of predicted bag, and examined this percentage in relation to raptor numbers at Langholm (Table 10.8, Figure 10.4). For all three sets of predictions, this calculated deviation showed a similar downward trend as raptor numbers increased (Langholm analysis: r_s=–0.94, P<0.05; moor G: r_s=–0.89, P<0.05; moor F: r_s=–0.89, P<0.05). So, the shortfall in grouse bags in later years was not only greater than expected, but also increased with raptor breeding numbers. Note that this relationship applied only to 1991–96 at Langholm, under the ratio of grouse/raptors prevailing at the time. Any change in this ratio could affect the pattern, together with the magnitude and direction of the deviations.

In summary, the shortfall from predicted bags at Langholm increased over the period 1993–96, coinciding with an increase in the numbers of breeding harriers and peregrines.

Were the low bags in 1993–96 due to undershooting?
The numbers of grouse shot in any one year are a function of the numbers shot on each day and the number of days' shooting. Because shooting days are usually booked in advance, it is desirable for grouse managers

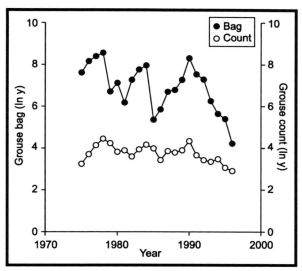

Figure 10.5 Numbers of grouse shot on Langholm moor during 1975–96 in comparison with an index count of relative abundance of grouse conducted by gamekeepers. Both bag and count data are transformed to natural logarithms

to have a good idea of the relative abundance of grouse from year to year. For this reason, transect counts of grouse in each July have been conducted by the gamekeepers at Langholm since 1975. These counts are not intended to estimate grouse density but to provide an index of abundance which is roughly comparable from year to year.

Annual grouse bags and an index of grouse abundance derived from the gamekeepers' July counts for the period 1975–1996 are shown in Figure 10.5, using log-transformed values. Not surprisingly, more grouse were shot in years when more grouse were counted by the gamekeepers, giving a strong positive correlation between the two sets of values (r=0.64, N=22, P<0.01). However, the relationship between bags and counts suggests that bags bore a lower relation to counts in low years than in high years. The amplitude of the fluctuations in grouse bags was much greater than the amplitude of the fluctuations in the numbers of grouse counted by the gamekeepers. This reflects a recognised curvilinear relationship between grouse density and the proportion of grouse shot, so that at low densities a smaller proportion of the population was shot than at high densities (Hudson 1985).

It could be argued that fewer grouse were shot in recent years because shooting effort was lower in relation to the numbers of grouse counted by the gamekeeper. We

tested for a change in shooting practice by comparing the pattern of points for 1991–96 with the fitted relationship between the log bag and the log gamekeepers' counts from 1975–90 (Figure 10.6). The points for 1993–96 all fell below the line. An analysis of covariance to test for a difference in intercepts between 1991–96 and 1975–90, assuming a common slope, gave $F_{1,19}=0.15$ (P=0.70), with no evidence of an effect. The corresponding test for equality of slopes gave $F_{1,18}=3.8$ (P=0.09), ie no firm evidence of reduced bags at low July counts. In other words, the statistical analysis showed no evidence for undershooting at Langholm in 1993–96.

Other considerations are relevant to shooting practice over the years. First, there is an assumption that the gamekeepers' counts were a consistent index of grouse density over this 22-year period. We had no way of assessing this for the period 1975–91, but between 1992 and 1996 the gamekeepers' July counts declined by an annual average of 14%, compared with 4% in our own

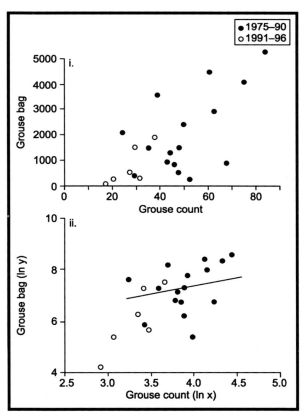

Figure 10.6 Relationship between grouse bags at Langholm and an index count of the relative abundance of grouse conducted by gamekeepers. Both bag and count data are shown as (i) untransformed values and (ii) transformed to natural logarithms. In (ii) a linear regression is fitted to the 1975–90 data (y=3.21+1.04x)

counts, a difference that was not statistically significant ($F_{1,6}$=2.59, P=0.16). Moreover, the two sets of counts did not cover exactly the same areas, and were not done on the same days as ours.

Another factor which could have altered the relationship between the keepers' July counts and the numbers of grouse subsequently shot was the increasing numbers of harriers on the moor in late summer. The keepers' counts were done three to four weeks before shooting began, within which period many grouse were removed by harriers in the later years, leaving fewer (relative to the July counts) for the guns in August. For example, in Chapter 8 we estimated that, in 1996, 25% of the grouse chicks present in mid-July were killed by harriers by mid-August. In other words, whatever the relationship between July counts and subsequent bags, this relationship would be expected to have changed as harrier numbers rose, giving the appearance in the records of 'undershooting'.

There were also changes in the number of shooting days during the study (which is one of the usual adjustments made to changes in grouse density). In 1994, it was agreed to conduct four days of driven shooting at Langholm in each of the remaining years of the study, with one day spent on each of the main grouse beats in each year. This plan was followed in 1994 and 1995, when bags of 284 and 221 grouse were shot respectively. Following a poor opening day in 1996, when only 34 grouse were shot, the Estate management, after consultation with the scientists, decided to shoot only one further day resulting in a total annual bag of 67 grouse. Two of the four main grouse beats at Langholm were not shot in 1996 and a full shooting programme would probably have approximately doubled the total bag. However, it is worth stressing that, under normal circumstances, a bag of 34 grouse from a full day's driven shooting would result in cancellation of further driven days. Even a bag of 134 grouse in 1996 would have been well below the confidence limits on predicted bags from each method of calculation.

To put this discussion of grouse bags into context, it is informative to compare the numbers of grouse shot in the last peak year of 1990 with the observed densities of grouse at Langholm in 1996, the year in which we predict that the grouse population should have peaked again. In 1990, 4038 grouse were shot at Langholm from 41.4 km² of heather, an average of 49 grouse per 0.5 km². In 1996, we estimated that July grouse densities averaged 27.8±3.6 grouse per 0.5 km². In other words, nearly twice as many grouse were shot for a given area in 1990 than were counted alive there before shooting in 1996.

DISCUSSION

Analysis of the Langholm grouse bags suggested three clear patterns. First, there has been a long-term decline in the numbers of grouse shot since early this century. Langholm grouse bags fluctuated around a higher level in the period before the second world war than during the post-war period. Trends in grouse bags during the period 1950–present also suggested a similar decline. In many respects, the decline in grouse bags at Langholm reflected wider patterns identified elsewhere by Barnes (1987) and Hudson (1992). These authors identified four distinct periods of grouse shooting:

- pre-1913, when moors were more productive and bags fluctuated but remained relatively stable;
- 1915–40, when bags recovered after the decline of the first world war and returned to previous levels;
- 1940–70, when bags again recovered after the second world war but to lower levels; and
- 1970–present, when bags generally declined, but with considerable regional variation.

What caused the long-term decline in grouse bags at Langholm? This is a difficult question to answer retrospectively. Comparison of aerial photographs taken in 1948 and 1988 indicated that heather-dominant vegetation declined by 48% during those 40 years (Chapter 2). The decline in heather cover was consistent with the effects of heavy grazing by sheep, with the heather being replaced by grass-dominant swards. Heather loss at Langholm appeared to have been rapid and to have parallelled widespread patterns across much of upland Britain (Thompson *et al.* 1995). The loss of nearly half of the heather-dominant moorland at Langholm seemed likely to have contributed to the long-term decline in the bags. Correlation does not mean causation, however, and other factors, including decreases in numbers of gamekeepers and increases in numbers of both avian and mammalian predators during this period, may have also contributed to the long-term decline in grouse bags.

The second pattern in the Langholm grouse bags was the tendency to fluctuate with a periodicity of six years. The cycle period of six years was in line with findings from other grouse moors in southern Scotland, Cumbria and Northumberland (Williams 1985; Hudson 1992), and fitted the trend for grouse cycle periods to increase towards the north and west (Hudson 1992). Causes of grouse population cycles have received much attention and for red grouse two competing views have emerged. The 'intrinsic' hypothesis suggests that changes in social structure and territorial behaviour within the grouse population cause cycles (Watson *et al.* 1994; Moss *et al.* 1996), whereas the 'extrinsic' hypothesis suggests that the effects of natural enemies such as the parasite *T. tenuis* on grouse survival and productivity generate cycles (Hudson *et al.* 1992; Dobson & Hudson 1992). We do not know if either or both of these processes caused the earlier population cycles at Langholm, but what does seem clear is that they were not caused by raptor predation because raptors did not breed in high numbers prior to 1993.

The third pattern to emerge from the Langholm grouse bags was that, following three pronounced cycles during the 1970s and 1980s, the numbers of grouse shot declined after the last peak in 1990 to a low level, but then failed to recover to a new peak as would have been expected. The observed six-year period of continuous decline in grouse bags was three times longer than any decline phase seen since the second world war, and,

excluding the declines during the war years, was unprecedented this century. Modelling the grouse bags at Langholm during 1991–96 on the basis of the observed grouse bags during 1950–90 showed that the bags during 1995 and 1996 were significantly lower than expected, and moreover they continued to decline even though they were expected to increase from 1993 to reach a peak in 1996. In fact, about twice as many grouse were shot per unit area at Langholm during the 1990 peak as were counted alive prior to shooting during July 1996.

Comparison of grouse bags from Langholm with two nearby moors where harriers and peregrines bred at densities considerably lower than at Langholm showed that the grouse bags in the three areas cycled in relative synchrony with a six-year periodicity during 1975–90. Since 1993, however, grouse bags at Langholm continued to decline whereas those on the two nearby moors rose to a high level. The implication was that the population cycle had continued on the nearby moors, whereas at Langholm the population was held in a prolonged trough. The evidence presented in the previous Chapters suggested that increases in raptor numbers and raptor predation at Langholm may have been the cause. Conversely, the increased bags on the nearby moors indicated that the presence of harriers and peregrines at low density did not prevent these grouse populations from increasing to levels allowing driven shooting. This latter suggestion was supported by the observed high grouse bags at Langholm during 1990 when two pairs of harriers bred successfully, and by the apparent relationship between the deviation from expected bags at Langholm during 1991–96 and the numbers of breeding raptors. Not surprisingly, the impact of raptors on grouse bags seemed to depend on the numbers of breeding raptors present.

Finally, it is helpful to put the grouse bags at Langholm into an economic context. The principal cost of grouse moor management lies in the employment and provisioning of gamekeepers, against which is balanced the revenue obtained from grouse shooting. Hudson (1992) developed an economic model which suggested that, at gamekeeper densities similar to those at Langholm (one keeper per 10 km^2), costs and income are balanced when 55 grouse are shot per km^2. On the basis of this model, an average of 2277 grouse must be shot annually from the 41.4 km^2 moor at Langholm to 'break even' financially. The actual cost in 1996 to the Buccleuch Estates of maintaining grouse moor management at Langholm was £99,500 (G Lewis, pers. comm.). The average price for driven grouse shooting in 1996 was £40 per bird, suggesting that a bag of 2487 grouse was required to balance costs, some 2420 more birds than were actually shot. The shortfall in the grouse bag during 1996 resulted in a net loss to the estate of £96,800. Such calculations consider grouse shooting in isolation from other forms of upland land use currently practised at Langholm, namely hill farming and forestry, but nevertheless give an indication of the scale of the financial loss.

Chapter 11

11. General discussion

In this final Chapter we pull together our results in an attempt to answer two questions.
- First, did raptors limit grouse densities at Langholm substantially below the level they would have achieved in the absence of raptors?
- Second, in the absence of any illegal control, would raptors limit grouse densities on other moors?

Throughout, we attempt to put the results of this study in a wider context, both in terms of other factors which influence grouse populations and also in relation to current views on the predator limitation of bird and mammal populations.

DID RAPTORS LIMIT GROUSE DENSITY AT LANGHOLM?

Long-term decline
It is first important to establish what has happened to the Langholm grouse population in the longer term. Bag records indicate that more grouse were shot prior to the second world war than after, and the limited information available for the period prior to the first world war suggests that bags were even larger then. What were the most likely causes of the long-term decline in grouse bags?

Almost certainly the decline had nothing to do with raptors. Whilst the recovery in the hen harrier population in mainland Britain started during the 1940s (Watson 1977), harriers were rarely seen at Langholm until the mid-1980s. Peregrine populations crashed nationally and locally during the 1950s and 1960s due largely to the effects of organochlorine pesticides (Ratcliffe 1993). As population levels of both harriers and peregrines were low in the post-war years, it seems very unlikely that they prevented grouse populations from recovering to densities which could be harvested at pre-war levels. It is possible that other predators of grouse increased in numbers during this time. Both foxes and corvids have probably increased countrywide, partly as a result of changing patterns of land use and partly as a result of declining numbers of gamekeepers (Hudson 1992).

Could habitat changes explain the long-term decline in grouse bags at Langholm? Analysis of aerial photographs taken at Langholm in 1948 and 1988 indicates that heather-dominant vegetation by 48% in this period, and that the most likely cause was heavy grazing by sheep. This grazing resulted in both a smaller total area of heather-dominant vegetation, and an increasing fragmentation of the remaining heather. The loss of such large areas of heather could well have been the major cause of the long-term decline in grouse bags.

Short-term decline
Following a productive season in 1990 when more than 4000 grouse were shot, grouse bags subsequently declined to a level where shooting became economically unviable. This decline coincided with an increase in the numbers of harriers and peregrines breeding on the moor. The six years of continuous decline in grouse bags were the longest since records began in 1913. A model based on the Langholm grouse bags from 1950 to 1990 suggested that the observed bags during 1995 and 1996 were significantly lower than expected. The model prediction that Langholm grouse bags should have increased to a cyclic peak in 1996 was supported by the increased bags on two neighbouring moors which formerly cycled in synchrony with Langholm. The most obvious difference between Langholm and the neighbouring moors in recent years was that Langholm had high breeding densities of harriers and peregrines, while the other moors had low densities of these raptors.

Evidence from both grouse bags and grouse counts indicated that the Langholm grouse population did not increase as expected. The key question is not whether raptors caused this recent decline, but whether raptors prevented the population from increasing to densities which would allow driven shooting. In this context, it is important to distinguish between the effects of predation upon the post-breeding population which is potentially available for shooting in autumn and upon the breeding population in spring. Both are now considered in turn.

Post-breeding densities in autumn

Raptor predation in summer reduced grouse densities in two ways:

- direct predation of chicks and adults
- indirect losses of potential chicks as a result of the deaths of their putative parents in spring.

Direct chick losses to hen harriers accounted for up to 37% of the chicks that successfully hatched. Most of these losses to harriers occurred after the early period of high chick losses (probably to starvation), and it thus appeared that they were largely additive to this early mortality. Similar conclusions were reached by Redpath (1991) in a previous study of harrier predation on grouse chicks on Highland moors. In some circumstances, such as on moors where the tick-borne virus that causes louping-ill is present, it is conceivable that late chick mortality will offset predation by hen harriers to some extent. However, louping-ill is a localised problem which occurs only in certain areas. In most red grouse populations, as in other gamebirds, chick mortality is highest during the first two weeks of life and is attributed to either starvation or poor weather (Erikstad & Spidsø 1982; Hudson 1986a; Bergerud 1988).

Of approximately equal importance to chick predation was a period of high predation on adult grouse during April and May, which reduced the grouse breeding population at Langholm by approximately 30%. This predation was almost entirely due to raptors, but whether harriers, peregrines or other raptors were responsible was undetermined. It occurred at a time when most grouse were paired and there appeared to be little scope for compensation through the replacement of territorial birds from any non-territorial 'surplus'. It remains unclear to what extent this predation on adult grouse could be compensated by reduction in other mortality.

In a natural situation, one would expect mortality due to other predators to increase in the absence of raptors, as was shown experimentally by Parker (1984) for willow ptarmigan. However, grouse moors are not natural situations, and foxes and mustelids are generally controlled by gamekeepers. It seems likely that the extent of any compensation due to increased mammalian predation will depend upon the intensity of keepering. Throughout the study, parasite burdens of grouse killed by predators were low at Langholm and it appeared unlikely that parasites had much influence on grouse numbers. However, if grouse densities increased in the absence of raptors, parasite burdens would probably increase and influence both grouse survival and productivity. In the past, the Langholm grouse population showed cyclic fluctuations of a periodicity similar to those in England for which parasites have been implicated as the causal factor (Hudson 1986, 1992; Hudson et al. 1992a, b).

If predation of adult grouse in early summer is such an important demographic event, why has it not been reported in other red grouse studies? High spring losses were not recorded during the early grouse studies at Glen Esk and Kerloch (Jenkins et al. 1963, 1964, 1967; Watson et al. 1984), possibly because predator densities were low when these studies were conducted. Fox predation on radio-tagged hens in spring was high (38%) throughout the Rickarton study during the 1980s (Moss et al. 1990), but was not thought to have caused the observed decline in grouse density (Moss et al. 1996). In Strathspey and Yorkshire, the numbers of grouse corpses recovered during carcase searching peaked during March and April; with deaths attributed mainly to predation in Strathspey and to parasites in Yorkshire (Hudson 1992). Hudson referred to this mortality as 'winter loss' and suggested that it reduced breeding density. The difference between this 'winter loss' and the 'summer loss' of our study is largely one of definition.

It has been suggested that recorded high mortality of adult red grouse in early summer is an artefact of radio-tagging (Watson & Moss 1990; A Watson, pers.

comm.; R Moss, pers. comm.). We know of no published evidence to support this assertion, and three lines of evidence to refute it. First, we found no difference in winter or summer survival between radio-tagged and wing-tagged grouse (Thirgood *et al.* 1995), in agreement with similar studies of willow ptarmigan (Schieck 1988), black grouse (Willebrand 1988) and pheasants (Marcström *et al.* 1988). Second, winter mortality rates estimated by radio-tagging were similar to mortality rates estimated by finds of grouse carcases (Thirgood *et al.* 1997). Finally, summer mortality rates of radio-tagged grouse were similar to the reduction in the numbers of adult grouse counted between April and July.

The combined effects of direct and indirect losses of grouse to raptors at Langholm during the summer appeared to reduce the numbers of grouse potentially available for shooting by around 50% within a single breeding season. This must remain a tentative conclusion as we have not conducted the predator removal experiments needed to prove it.

Breeding densities in spring

If raptor predation in summer reduced autumn densities by 50% within a single breeding season, did this have any effect on breeding densities in subsequent springs? We used our estimates of summer loss combined with the observed density dependence in winter loss in a simple model to predict subsequent spring densities in the absence of summer raptor predation. Although there were uncertainties in the model, it suggested that spring densities of grouse in the absence of summer raptor predation would increase to a level 1.3 times that found in the presence of raptors. Similarly, the model predicted that breeding production in the absence of raptors would increase to a level 2.5 times that found in the presence of raptors. The model did not incorporate the observed density dependence in summer loss of adults or any delayed density dependence, so its usefulness in making longer-term predictions of equilibrium grouse densities in the absence of raptors was limited. However, it did suggest that both breeding densities and breeding production would increase in the absence of summer raptor predation, a suggestion which could be tested experimentally.

There has been considerable debate as to whether predation on grouse in winter reduces breeding densities the following spring (Hudson 1990; Watson & Moss 1990). Early studies on moors where grouse were at high density showed that winter predation was entirely compensatory and merely removed part of the 'doomed surplus' (Jenkins *et al.* 1963, 1964; Watson 1985), whereas more recent studies on moors where grouse were at low density demonstrated that winter predation was not restricted to non-territorial grouse and could result in reductions in breeding density (Hudson 1992).

Although we were able to document the extent, timing and cause of winter mortality, we were unable to determine the amount by which it reduced spring breeding densities. Predation was not confined to non-territorial grouse, at least in the latter half of the winter, and by that time there appeared to be few surplus birds in the population which could replace territorial birds that were killed. However, our counting sites persistently gained birds through immigration during the winter, and these birds presumably compensated locally some of the losses to raptors. We do not know where these birds came from or whether, before arrival, they were territorial or non-territorial. At the scale of our counting sites, movement of grouse could theoretically compensate between 55% and 95% of the winter mortality. At the scale of the wider population, however, the extent of compensation through movement was unknown, because we could not know whether birds which moved in winter increased their breeding success over what it would otherwise have been. It seemed likely that some of the winter raptor predation was additive and thus reduced breeding density, particularly that which occurred in late winter. If reduced winter predation did result in higher breeding densities, however, some parasite-induced reduction in productivity may have followed, at least in some years (Hudson 1986a, b; Hudson *et al.* 1992a, b).

Habitat and grouse demography

The conversion of heather to rough grassland, attributed to heavy grazing by sheep, has almost certainly played a role in the long-term decline of grouse bags at Langholm. But does habitat currently influence grouse demography and, in particular, does poor-quality habitat make grouse more susceptible to predation? We found no evidence that the measured features of the habitat directly influenced predation on adult grouse. The habitat characteristics which we measured had no influence on the numbers of grouse found dead on our counting sites or on the likelihood that radio-tagged grouse would be killed in winter. Habitat appeared to have a more subtle influence on overwinter losses, however, with lower losses occurring on areas with more heather. We interpreted this as an indication that grouse moved into areas with more heather, possibly following the deaths of other birds. However, we have no evidence of such movements from our radio-tagged grouse which were caught mainly in the core of the moor. If grouse move preferentially into areas of good habitat and by doing so improve their breeding success, then some winter predation could be compensated.

We found little evidence that grouse breeding performance varied in relation to habitat at the scale of our counting sites. Females on areas with little heather produced on average as many chicks as females on areas with much heather. However, L Parkinson *et al.* (unpublished data) demonstrated, with a small sample of radio-tagged hens, that chick survival in the first two weeks of life was related to the use of boggy vegetation and suggested that this was due to the abundance of invertebrates in these habitats, thus confirming the findings of earlier studies (Savory 1977; Hudson 1986a). The extent to which chick survival could be improved at Langholm through habitat management is unknown but clearly remains a key area for further research. Recent work on black grouse showed that density and breeding success were higher on lightly grazed than heavily grazed moors, irrespective of the presence of a gamekeeper, and that this was related to the development of taller vegetation providing cover for chicks and higher densities of invertebrates (Baines 1996). The role of habitat in providing red grouse chicks with cover from aerial predators such as harriers remains unclear. Harriers were more likely to attack grouse broods in areas with a mixture of heather and grass than in pure heather, but we could not say whether this was due to habitat selection by foraging harriers or increased detectability of broods in grass/heather mixtures. Areas with mosaics of boggy and tall vegetation presumably offered the best prospects for broods.

Limitation or regulation?

The data were strongly suggestive that raptor predation in summer, and possibly also in winter, reduced both the breeding density and the post-breeding surplus of grouse available for shooting. The Langholm grouse population appeared to be at a new equilibrium density, lower than in the absence of raptors, and too low to allow an economically viable harvest. Raptor predation appeared the most likely process to have set this new equilibrium and, as such, could be considered a limiting factor. But did raptor predation regulate the grouse population?

Regulatory factors are those which act in a density-dependent manner, and serve to return a population to equilibrium following perturbation. We identified two density-dependent processes in the current study, namely winter and early summer loss of adult grouse, and suggested that both were largely due to raptor predation. There appeared to be a single pattern of density dependence applying both across sites within years and across years within sites. The extent to which raptor predation was regulating the grouse population at Langholm depends upon the strength of the density dependence in relation to density-independent factors, such as weather, which also affected the population. We are restricted in what we can conclude about population regulation through raptor predation by the short timescale of the current study and the relatively small temporal variation in grouse densities observed. If the grouse population were to undergo a major perturbation, caused for example by a poor breeding season or high shooting mortality, we might find that reduced winter loss could quickly return the population to its current level.

How do our conclusions regarding raptor limitation of the Langholm grouse population fit with current views on predator limitation of vertebrate populations in general? The classical view of Errington (1946), that vertebrate populations were limited by habitat constraints and that predators took only a 'doomed surplus', dominated discussions on predation for decades, and was supported by the early studies on red grouse (Jenkins *et al.* 1963, 1964). Newton (1993) recently reviewed the role of predation in limiting bird populations and concluded that, although mortality due to predation was unlikely to be compensatory always, many bird populations have reservoirs of non-breeders which can replace territorial birds lost to predators. He concluded that two groups of ground-nesting birds – waterfowl and gamebirds – appear to be particularly prone to limitation by predation. Amongst the gamebirds, only for black grouse and capercaillie (Marcström *et al.* 1988) and grey partridge (Tapper *et al.* 1996) have experiments demonstrated that increased breeding success as a result of predator removal also resulted in increased breeding density. The predators removed were foxes and martens in the first study and foxes, stoats and corvids in the second. Newton (1993) made two further relevant points. First, in experiments where only one predator species was removed, there was usually little increase in prey density because of compensatory-increased predation by other species. Second, in some experiments predation was influenced by the availability of alternative prey and nesting cover. A third additional point was that these experiments did not involve the removal of raptors, although there is no inherent reason why removal of generalist raptors would have given different results.

To our knowledge, only one study has examined the effects of a reduction in raptor numbers on prey populations, in this case kestrels and Tengmalm's owls preying on three species of small mammals (Norrdahl & Korpimäki 1995). Raptor densities were reduced by removing stick-nests and filling nest cavities before the breeding season commenced. The conclusion was that breeding raptors did not regulate their prey populations in the long term, but probably caused short-term changes in the population dynamics of all three prey species. The densities of one vole species actually decreased in the raptor reduction areas apparently due to increased weasel predation in the absence of predation on weasels by Tengmalm's owls.

In general, there appears to be an emerging consensus that predation can, in some circumstances, both limit and regulate vertebrate populations. This view appears to have been fairly widely accepted by researchers investigating the three- to four-year cyclic fluctuations of microtine rodents in Scandinavia and North America, the ten-year snowshoe hare cycle in North America, and the periodic irruptions of mice and rabbits in Australia (reviewed by Boutin 1995; Krebs *et al.* 1995; Stenseth, Bjornstad & Falck 1996; Pech, Sinclair & Newsome 1995). Currently, the consensus for birds is that predation plays a relatively minor role in the direct limitation of breeding densities of most species that have been studied, with the exception of waterfowl and gamebirds for which there is experimental evidence that predation can in some circumstances limit both breeding densities and breeding success (Newton 1993).

WOULD RAPTORS LIMIT GROUSE DENSITIES ON OTHER MOORS?
Whilst our data were strongly suggestive that raptors were indeed limiting the grouse population at Langholm, can we also conclude that limitation could occur on other grouse moors in the absence of illegal control of raptors? We first need to understand why so many grouse were killed by raptors at Langholm, and why this appeared to have a large impact on that particular grouse population.

Numerical response
The first answer to the question of why so many grouse were killed by raptors at Langholm is that both breeding and winter densities of harriers and peregrines were high, while grouse densities were relatively low, giving a high raptor/grouse ratio. Once protected from illegal control, local breeding harrier numbers increased markedly, from two to 14 pairs in five years. In the absence of human interference, the numbers of meadow pipits and small mammals were the primary factors influencing the breeding densities of harriers. Thus, moors with high densities of meadow pipits and small

mammals attracted many harriers, and this pattern also held within moors between years. Within our sample of study moors, meadow pipit abundance was primarily influenced by latitude, and, within the Langholm area, there was a tendency for meadow pipit numbers to increase as heather cover declined below 70%. Meadow pipit preference for heather/grass mixtures was also found by Coulson and Whittaker (1978) and Howarth and Thompson (1990). Small mammals, particularly field voles, were most abundant in areas of rough grassland and least abundant in heather-dominant areas. In other words, the highest densities of the harriers' small prey, and therefore the harriers themselves, were found on relatively southern moors, such as Langholm, which also had a high ratio of grass/heather. The mosaic of heather and grassland found at Langholm, most likely a product of heavy grazing by sheep in the recent past, appeared to provide an ideal breeding habitat for harriers.

Harrier numbers did not vary in accordance with grouse densities during the breeding season and we did not find that the breeding success of female harriers was influenced by the abundance of grouse. Male harriers, however, produced more chicks on moors with higher grouse densities, apparently as a result of increased bigamy on these moors. The implication was that males were attracted to grassy moors by high densities of small prey, but females were more likely to mate with bigamous males in areas with high grouse abundance. Presumably, as females in bigamous trios receive fewer food items to feed their chicks, they could breed in this way only where large prey such as grouse chicks were relatively abundant. Hence, grassy moors with some intact heather and grouse should support high densities of harriers and high female/male ratios of harriers. On more heather-dominated moors, harriers bred at lower overall density, because males could settle there only at low density.

The breeding density of peregrines was also high at Langholm and fitted the national trend for breeding densities to decline northwards. Ratcliffe (1993) suggested that peregrines were more widely spaced in the north because of a reduced abundance of racing pigeons. With the exception of the apparent relationship between meadow pipit abundance and latitude noted above, there is little evidence of other upland bird species decreasing in abundance with latitude (Hudson 1988; Ratcliffe 1990). Peregrine breeding success also decreased with latitude, a trend previously noted by Ratcliffe (1993), and also attributed to the decreased availability of racing pigeons.

In contrast to the situation during summer, grouse densities in winter did appear to influence the numbers of female harriers seen at Langholm in winter, and this was consistent with the finding that both grouse densities and small mammal abundance influenced where female harriers hunted within the moor. The numbers of harriers sighted overwinter were not related to breeding numbers or success in the previous summer, despite the great variation observed at Langholm over the five years of the study. This implied that, within geographical regions, estates which killed harriers during the breeding season may not reduce harrier numbers overwinter and, conversely, estates which leave their harriers may suffer no greater predation in the following winter. However, very few harriers were seen overwinter in an earlier study in the Yorkshire Dales (Hudson 1990), which may be a reflection of the very low harrier breeding densities in this general region (Gibbons et al. 1993). On this larger scale, breeding numbers may influence overwintering numbers.

In summary, one clear reason why many grouse were killed by raptors throughout the year at Langholm was that breeding and overwintering numbers of harriers and peregrines were high. Breeding numbers of harriers were influenced mainly by meadow pipit and small mammal abundance, whilst breeding numbers of peregrines were probably influenced by racing pigeon abundance. Winter numbers of harriers appeared to be influenced by grouse availability rather than by local harrier breeding numbers or success the previous summer. The apparently trite answer that many grouse were killed by raptors because there were many raptors is of great significance in predicting whether or not we would expect similar predation rates on other moors.

Functional response

Both harriers and peregrines are generalist predators and eat a variety of prey species. During the summer on grouse moors, meadow pipits and grouse are the main prey of harriers, and pigeons and grouse are the main prey of peregrines. Whilst grouse are not numerically the most important prey for either species, the way in which the proportion of grouse increases in the diet of harriers and peregrines as grouse density increases – the functional response – has important implications for the impact of predation on the grouse population. The relationship between male harrier provisioning of grouse chicks and grouse chick density appeared to be sigmoidal, implying a 'Type III' functional response. This suggests that male harriers switch their hunting patterns to search for grouse chicks as grouse densities increase. This idea fits the observations of Redpath (1992), who found that harriers hunted habitats utilised by meadow pipits when grouse were scarce but hunted habitats utilised by grouse when grouse were abundant.

The shape of the functional response is important because the accelerating part of the curve at low grouse density results in density-dependent predation, whilst the decelerating part of the curve at high grouse density results in inverse density-dependent predation. In the case of male harriers and grouse chicks, predation was density dependent up to densities of 70 chicks per km², although further data are required at high grouse densities to see whether the curve really does level off, as the only data available are from two harrier nests on one moor in one year (Picozzi 1978). In terms of the impact on grouse populations, the greatest percentage of grouse chicks removed per harrier would be around 70 chicks per km². Assuming an average brood size after initial chick loss of six chicks, harrier predation would have its greatest impact at grouse densities around 12 pairs per km². Above this density, the proportion of grouse chicks removed by individual harriers should decline. This conclusion is tentative, however, because the harrier functional response was estimated from a number of different grouse moors, and, as noted above, we had few data at high grouse densities. However, the critical accelerating part of the functional response

curve indicating density-dependent predation of grouse chicks was determined from intensive observations conducted at one moor (Langholm) over four breeding seasons.

The extent to which harriers, particularly females, took grouse chicks was also influenced by the breeding system of the harriers. Both male and female harriers in bigamous relationships provisioned their nestlings with grouse chicks at a greater rate than those in monogamous relationships, presumably because grouse chicks were large profitable prey items which could compensate for reduced overall provisioning rates per nest. Bigamy in harriers was apparently related to grouse density and occurred more frequently at densities over 50 chicks per km². It appears that small prey were abundant at Langholm and attracted large numbers of harriers, whilst grouse were at an intermediate density, high enough to encourage bigamous breeding in harriers but too low to escape density-dependent chick predation.

The importance of grouse in the summer diet of peregrines also increased in relation to grouse abundance but the relationship appeared to be asymptotic (Type II) rather than sigmoidal. The shape of the peregrine functional response to grouse suggested that individual peregrines removed the greatest proportion of grouse at grouse densities below 10 pairs per km², declining at greater grouse densities. There was also a tendency for individual peregrines to eat more grouse at higher latitudes, so that at any given grouse density a peregrine in the Highlands would eat more grouse than a peregrine in the Borders or northern England.

In summary, the second reason why so many grouse were killed by raptors at Langholm and that raptor predation appeared to limit the grouse population was that grouse densities were very close to the level at which predation by both individual harriers and individual peregrines would remove the largest proportion of the grouse population. This was particularly the case for harriers, where grouse densities appeared to be high enough to encourage bigamy but too low to escape density-dependent predation.

Would a similar impact of raptor predation be expected on other grouse moors?

If illegal control of harriers and peregrines stopped on other grouse moors, would raptors have the same effect on grouse as at Langholm? While this is a difficult question to answer with any certainty, our current understanding of the numerical and functional responses of harriers and peregrines outlined above allows us to make some tentative predictions.

- As harrier breeding densities were influenced mainly by the abundance of small prey, namely meadow pipits and field voles, high densities of harriers would be most likely to occur on moors with a mosaic of heather and grassland, as is now typical of many moors in the Borders and northern England, subjected to heavy sheep grazing. Such conditions would be less likely to occur on moors with almost continuous heather cover, which are now found mainly in the Highlands (Thompson *et al*. 1995).

- Peregrines would also be expected to reach the highest breeding densities on southern moors as a result of the greater availability of racing pigeons there.

- Grouse populations at spring densities below 12 breeding pairs per km² would probably be most susceptible to limitation by harrier and peregrine predation.

For all these reasons, the impact of harriers and peregrines on grouse populations is likely to be higher on southern rather than northern moors, and on grassy rather than heather-dominated moors. It also appears that relatively low-density grouse populations will be more susceptible to limitation through predation than high-density grouse populations.

An illustration of the likely variation in the impact of harriers and peregrines on grouse moors may be gained by comparing Langholm to two nearby moors in Cumbria. At Langholm, both harrier and peregrine numbers increased over a five-year period, during which time grouse densities and bags remained low. In contrast, grouse bags increased markedly over the same time period on moors F and G to levels sustaining

driven shooting. Harriers and peregrines attempted to breed at low densities on both of these moors during this time, but breeding success of harriers was poor. The reasons for these breeding failures were unknown, but illegal control was suspected by the RSPB. We had no information on the abundance of grouse, passerines or small mammals on these moors, or on the extent of the replacement of heather-dominant vegetation with grasses, and therefore could make no comment on their suitability for harriers. Nonetheless, irrespective of the causes of low densities and poor breeding success of raptors on moors F and G, these moors illustrated that such low densities of harriers and peregrines were compatible with driven grouse shooting.

A further example of a moor where low densities of raptors did not prevent an economically viable harvest of grouse was moor C in NE Scotland. Harrier numbers here increased for two years following protection in 1989, but then subsequently declined to the present situation in 1996 of no breeding females. Peregrine numbers on this moor also declined from three to two pairs during this time. The reasons for these declines were unknown, but they were not caused by illegal control within this estate. Passerine and small mammal densities were low on this moor throughout the study and would lead us to expect low harrier densities. Grouse densities on moor C consistently increased throughout this period, and in 1996 over 1400 grouse were shot. Moor C thus provided further evidence that it was possible to produce driven grouse shooting with low densities of breeding harriers and peregrines.

In summary, our data suggest that, in the absence of illegal control of raptors, the impacts of harriers and peregrines are likely to be highest on low-density grouse populations on southern, grassy grouse moors. However, this prediction is tentative, and it is likely that considerable local and regional variation will occur.

POSTSCRIPT

As we go to press, we are able to include information on the 1997 breeding season at Langholm, thus bringing the story fully up to date. In a year when vole numbers were high, the numbers of hen harrier females attempting to breed within the study area increased to 20, with a total of 66 harrier chicks fledged from 17 successful nests. Peregrine breeding numbers were similar to 1996 with six pairs, but breeding success was poor with only four chicks fledged. Grouse densities in April were similar to those in previous years at 14.7 ± 1.8 adult grouse per 0.5 km^2. However, a combination of high summer loss of adult grouse (July density 9.9 ± 0.8 adult grouse per 0.5 km^2) and poor breeding production (July density 11.6 ± 1.2 grouse chicks per 0.5 km^2) resulted in low densities of grouse in late July (July density 21.5 ± 1.8 grouse per 0.5 km^2). These July densities represented a 23% decline on those of the previous year. Four days of driven shooting were conducted at Langholm in late August with a total bag of 51 grouse. It seems clear that no recovery in grouse densities or bags occurred in 1997.

References

Angelstam, P., Lindström, E. & Widén, P. 1984. Role of predation in short-term fluctuations of some birds and mammals in Fennoscandia. *Oecologia (Berlin),* **62**, 199–208.

Baines, D. 1996. The implications of grazing and predator management on the habitats and breeding success of black grouse *Tetrao tetrix. Journal of Applied Ecology,* **33**, 54–63.

Barnes, R.W. 1987. Long term declines of red grouse in Scotland. *Journal of Applied Ecology,* **24**, 735–741.

Begon, M., Harper, J.L. & Townsend, C.R. 1996. *Ecology – individuals, populations and communities.* Oxford: Blackwell Scientific.

Bergerud, A.T. 1988. Population ecology of North American grouse. In: *Adaptive strategies and population ecology of northern grouse,* edited by A.T. Bergerud & M.W. Gratson, 578–685. Minneapolis: University of Minnesota Press.

Beske, A.E. 1982. Local and migratory movements of radio-tagged juvenile harriers. *Raptor Research,* **16**, 39–53.

Bibby, C.J. & Etheridge, B. 1993. Status of the hen harrier *Circus cyaneus* in Scotland 1988–89. *Bird Study,* **40**, 1–11.

Bibby, C.J., Burgess, N.D. & Hill, D.A. 1992. *Bird census techniques.* London: Academic Press.

Bildstein, K.L. 1992. Causes and consequences of reversed sexual size dimorphism in raptors: the head start hypothesis. *Journal of Raptor Research,* **26**, 115–123.

Brom, T.G. 1986. Microscopic identification of feathers and feather fragments of palearctic birds. *Bijdragen tot de Dierkunde,* **56**, 181–204.

Box, G.E. & Jenkins, G.H. 1970. *Time-series analysis. Forecasting and control.* San Fransisco: Holden-Day.

Boutin, S. 1995. Testing predator–prey theory by studying fluctuating populations of small mammals. *Wildlife Research,* **22**, 89–100.

Collopy, M.W. & Bildstein, K.L. 1987. Foraging behavior of northern harriers wintering in southeastern salt and freshwater marshes. *The Auk,* **104**, 11–16.

Côté, I.M. & Sutherland, W.J. 1997. The effectiveness of removing predators to protect bird populations. *Conservation Biology,* **11**, 395–405.

Coulson, J.C. & Whittaker, J.B. 1978. The ecology of moorland animals. In: *Production ecology of British moors and mantain grasslands,* edited by O. W. Heal & D.F. Perkins, 53–93. Berlin: Springer-Verlag.

Cramp, S. & Simmons, K.E.L. 1980. *Handbook of the birds of Europe, the Middle East and North Africa, vol. 2.* Oxford: Oxford University Press.

Crawley, M.J., ed. 1992. *Natural enemies – the population biology of predators, parasites and diseases.* Oxford: Blackwell Scientific.

Crick, H.A.P. & Ratcliffe, D.A. 1995. The peregrine, *Falco peregrinus,* breeding population of the United Kingdom in 1991. *Bird Study,* **42**, 1–19.

Day, M.G. 1966. Identification of hair and feather remains in the gut and faeces of stoats and weasels. *Journal of Zoology,* **148**, 201–217.

Dobson, A.P. & Hudson, P.J. 1992. Regulation and stability of a free-living host–parasite system: *Trichostrongylus tenuis* in red grouse. II. Population models. *Journal of Animal Ecology,* **61**, 487–498.

Dobson, A.P. & Hudson, P.J. 1995. The interaction between the parasites and predators of red grouse. *Ibis,* **137**, Suppl. 1, 87–96.

Erikstad, K.E. 1985. Growth and survival of willow grouse chicks in relation to home range size, brood movements and habitat selection. *Ornis Scandinavica,* **16**, 181–190.

Erikstad, K.E. & Spidsø, T. 1982. The influence of weather on food intake, insect prey selection and feeding behaviour in willow grouse chicks in northern Norway. *Ornis Scandinavica,* **13**, 176–182.

Errington, P.L. 1946. Predation and vertebrate populations. *Quarterly Review of Biology,* **21**, 144–177.

Etheridge, B., Summers, R.W. & Green, R. 1997. The effects of human persecution on the population dynamics of hen harriers *Circus cyaneus* nesting in Scotland. *Journal of Applied Ecology,* **34**, 1081–1106.

Gibbons, D.W., Reid, J.B. & Chapman, R.A. 1993. *The new atlas of breeding birds in Britain and Ireland.* London: Poyser.

Hagen, Y. 1969. Norwegian studies on the reproduction of birds of prey and owls in relation to micro-rodent population fluctuation. *Fauna,* **22**, 73–126.

Hamerstrom, F. 1986. *Harrier, hawk of the marsh: the hawk that is ruled by a mouse.* Washington, DC: Smithsonian Institute Press.

Hamilton, Lord. 1922. *Forty years on.* London: Hodder & Stoughton.

Hanski, I., Hansson, L. & Henttonen, H. 1991. Specialist predators, generalist predators and the microtine vole cycle. *Journal of Animal Ecology,* **60**, 353–367.

Harvie-Brown, J.A. 1906. *The fauna of the Tay Basin and Strathmore.* Edinburgh: David Douglas.

Hewson, R. 1986. The distribution and density of fox dens and the effects of management. *Journal of Applied Ecology,* **23**, 531–538.

Holling, C.S. 1959. Some characteristics of simple types of predation and parasitism. *Canadian Entomologist,* **91**, 385–398.

Howarth, P.F. & Thompson, D.B.A. 1990. Factors associated with the breeding distribution of upland birds in the south Pennines, England. *Journal of Applied Ecology,* **27**, 562–577.

Hudson, P.J. 1985. Harvesting red grouse in the north of England. In: *Game harvest management,* edited by S.L.Beasom & S.F. Robertson, 319–326.

Kingsville, Texas: Caesar Kleberg Institute.

Hudson, P.J. 1986a. *Red grouse: the biology and management of a wild gamebird.* Fordingbridge: The Game Conservancy Trust.

Hudson, P.J. 1986b. The effect of a parasitic nematode on the breeding production of red grouse. *Journal of Animal Ecology,* **55,** 85–92.

Hudson, P.J. 1988. Spatial variations, patterns and management options in upland bird communities. In: *Ecological change in the uplands,* edited by M.B. Usher & D.B.A. Thompson, 381–399. Oxford: Blackwell Scientific.

Hudson, P.J. 1990. Territorial status and survival in a low density grouse population: preliminary observations and experiments. In: *Red grouse population processes,* edited by A.N.Lance & J.H.Lawton, 20–28. Sandy, Beds: Royal Society for the Protection of Birds.

Hudson, P.J. 1992. *Grouse in space and time – the population biology of a managed gamebird.* Fordingbridge: The Game Conservancy Trust.

Hudson, P.J. & Dobson, A.P. 1990. Red grouse population cycles and the population dynamics of the caecal nematode *Trichostrongylus tenuis.* In: *Red grouse population processes,* edited by A.N.Lance & J.H.Lawton, 5–20. Sandy, Beds: Royal Society for the Protection of Birds.

Hudson, P.J. & Newborn, D. 1995. *A manual of red grouse and moorland management.* Fordingbridge: The Game Conservancy Trust.

Hudson, P.J., Dobson, A.P. & Newborn, D. 1985. Cyclic and non-cyclic populations of red grouse: a role for parasites? In: *Ecology and genetics of host–parasite interactions,* edited by D. Rollinson & R.M.Anderson, 77–89. London: Academic Press for the Linnean Society.

Hudson, P.J., Dobson, A.P. & Newborn, D. 1992a. Do parasites make prey vulnerable to predation? Red grouse and parasites. *Journal of Animal Ecology,* **61,** 681–692.

Hudson, P.J., Dobson, A.P. & Newborn, D. 1992b. Regulation and stability of a free-living host-parasite system: *Trichostrongylus tenuis* in red grouse. I Monitoring and parasite reductions. *Journal of Animal Ecology,* **61,** 477–486.

Hudson, P.J., Newborn, D. & Robertson, P.A. 1997. Geographical and seasonal patterns of mortality in red grouse populations. *Wildlife Biology.* In press.

Hudson, P.J., Norman, R., Laurenson, M.K., Newborn, D., Gaunt, M., Jones, L., Reid, H., Gould, E., Bowers, R. & Dobson, A. 1995. Persistence in tick-borne viruses: *Ixodes ricinus* and louping ill in red grouse. *Parasitology,* **111,** S49–S58.

Jenkins, D., Watson, A. & Miller G.R. 1963. Population studies on red grouse, *Lagopus lagopus scoticus* (Lath.) in north-east Scotland. *Journal of Animal Ecology,* **32,** 317–376.

Jenkins, D., Watson, A. & Miller G.R. 1964. Predation and red grouse. *Journal of Applied Ecology,* **1,** 183–195.

Jenkins, D., Watson, A. & Miller G.R. 1967. Population fluctuations in the red grouse *Lagopus lagopus scoticus. Journal of Animal Ecology,* **36,** 97–122.

Kaplan, E.L. & Meier, P. 1958. Nonparametric estimation from incomplete observations. *Journal of the American Statistical Association,* **53,** 457–481.

Keith, L.B. & Rusch, D.H. 1988. Predation's role in the cyclic fluctuations of ruffed grouse. *Proceedings of the XIX International Ornithologists Congress,* vol. 1, 699–732.

Keith, L.B., Todd, A.W., Brand, C.J., Adamcik, R.S. & Rusch, D.H. 1977. An analysis of predation during a cyclic fluctuation of snowshoe hares. *XIII International Congress of Game Biologists,* 151–175.

Kenward, R.E. 1986. Problems of goshawk predation on pigeons and other game. *XVIII International Ornithological Congress,* 666–677.

Kenward, R.E. 1987. *Wildlife radio tagging.* London: Academic Press.

Kenward, R.E., Marcström, V. & Karlbom, M. 1981 Goshawk winter ecology in Swedish pheasant habitats. *Journal of Wildlife Management,* **45,** 397–408.

Korpimäki, E. 1985. Rapid tracking of microtine populations by their avian predators: possible evidence for stabilising predation. *Oikos,* **45,** 281–284.

Korpimäki, E. & Norrdahl, K. 1991. Numerical and functional responses of kestrels, short-eared owls and long-eared owls to vole densities. *Ecology,* **72,** 814–826.

Krebs, C.J. 1985. Do changes in spacing behaviour drive population cycles in small mammals? In: *Behavioural ecology,* edited by R.M.Sibly & R.H.Smith, 295–312. Oxford: Blackwell Scientific.

Krebs, C.J., Boutin, S., Boonstra, R., Sinclair, A.R.E., Smith, J.N.M., Dale, M.R.T. & Turkington, R. 1995. Impact of food and predation on the snowshoe hare cycle. *Science,* **269,** 1112–1115.

Lawton, J.H. 1990. Red grouse populations and moorland management. In: *Red grouse population processes,* edited by A.N.Lance & J.H.Lawton, 84–99. Sandy, Beds: Royal Society for the Protection of Birds.

Lindström, E., Andrén, H., Angelstam, P., Cederlund, G., Hornfeldt, B., Jäderberg, L., Lemnell, P.A., Martinsson, B., Sköld, K. & Swenson, J. 1994. Disease reveals the predator: sarcoptic mange, red fox predation and prey populations. *Ecology,* **75,** 1042–1049.

Lovat, Lord. 1911. *The grouse in health and disease.* London: Committee of Enquiry on Grouse Disease.

Mackenzie, J.M.D. 1952. Fluctuations in the numbers of British tetraonids. *Journal of Animal Ecology,* **21,** 128–153.

Manly, B., McDonald, L. & Thomas, D. 1993. *Resource selection by animals – statistical design* *and analysis for field studies.* London: Chapman and Hall.

Marcström, V., Engren, E. & Kenward, R.E. 1988. The impact of predation on boreal tetraonids during vole cycles – an experimental study. *Journal of Animal Ecology,* **57,** 859–872.

Marquiss, M. 1980. Habitat and diet of male and female hen harriers in Scotland in Winter. *British Birds,* **73,** 555–560.

Mearns, R. & Newton, I. 1988. Factors affecting breeding success of peregrines in south Scotland. *Journal of Animal Ecology,* **57,** 903–916.

Middleton, A.D. 1934. Periodic fluctuations in British game bird records. *Journal of Animal Ecology,* **3,** 231–249.

Miller, G.R., Watson, A. & Jenkins, D. 1970. Responses of red grouse populations to experimental improvement of their food. In: *Animal populations in relation to their food resources,* edited by A. Watson, 323–334. (Symposia of the British Ecological Society, 10.) Oxford: Blackwell Scientific.

Moss, R. 1969 A comparison of red grouse (*Lagopus l. scoticus*) stocks with the production and nutritive value of heather (*Calluna vulgaris*). *Journal of Animal Ecology,* **38,** 103–112.

Moss, R. & Watson, A. 1985. Adaptive value of spacing behaviour in population cycles of red grouse and other animals. In: *Behavioural ecology. Ecological consequences of adaptive behaviour,* edited by R.M. Sibley & R.H. Smith, 275–294. Oxford: Blackwell Scientific.

Moss, R., Watson, A. & Parr, R. 1975. Maternal nutrition and breeding success in red grouse (*Lagopus lagopus scoticus*). *Journal of Animal Ecology,* **44,** 233–244.

Moss, R., Watson, A. & Parr, R. 1996. Experimental prevention of a population cycle in red grouse. *Ecology,* **77,** 1512–1530.

Moss, R., Watson, A. & Rothery, P. 1984. Inherent changes in the body size, viability and behaviour of a fluctuating red grouse population. *Journal of Animal Ecology,* **53,** 171–189.

Moss, R., Shaw, J.L., Watson, A. & Trenholm, I.B. 1990. Role of the caecal threadworm *Trichostrongylus tenuis* in the population dynamics of red grouse. In: *Red grouse population processes,* edited by A.N.Lance & J.H.Lawton, 62–71. Sandy, Beds: Royal Society for the Protection of Birds.

Moss, R., Watson, A., Rothery, P. & Glennie, W. 1981. Clutch size, egg size, hatch weight and laying date in relation to early mortality in red grouse (*Lagopus lagopus scoticus*). *Ibis,* **123,** 450–462.

Mountford, M.D., Watson, A., Moss, R., Parr, R. & Rothery, P. 1990. Land inheritance and population cycles of red grouse. In: *Red grouse population processes,* edited by A.N.Lance & J.H.Lawton, 78–83. Sandy, Beds: Royal Society for the Protection of Birds.

Murdoch, W.W. 1994. Population regulation in theory and practice. *Ecology,* **75,** 271–287.

Nethersole-Thompson, D. 1951. *The greenshank.* (New Naturalist series.) London: Collins.

Newton, I. 1979. *The population ecology of raptors.* Berkhamsted: Poyser Press.

Newton, I. 1993. Predation and limitation of bird numbers. *Current Ornithology,* **11,** 143–198.

Norrdahl, H. & Korpimäki, E. 1995. Effects of predator removal on vertebrate prey populations: birds of prey and small mammals. *Oecologia (Berlin),* **103,** 241–248.

Parker, H. 1984. Effect of corvid removal on reproduction of willow ptarmigan and black grouse. *Journal of Wildlife Management,* **48,** 1197–1205.

Pech, R.P., Sinclair, A.R.E. & Newsome, A.E. 1995. Predation models for primary and secondary prey species. *Wildlife Research,* **22,** 55–64.

Picozzi, N. 1968. Grouse bags in relation to the management and geology of heather moors. *Journal of Applied Ecology,* **5,** 483–488.

Picozzi, N. 1978. Dispersion, breeding and prey of the hen harrier (*Circus cyaneus*) in Glen Dye, Kincardineshire. *Ibis,* **120,** 489–509.

Picozzi, N. 1984. Breeding biology of polygynous hen harriers *Circus c. cyaneus* in Orkney. *Ornis Scandinavica,* **15,** 1–10.

Pollock, K.H., Winterstein, S.R., Bunck, C.M. & Curtis, P.D. 1989. Survival analysis in telemetry studies: the staggered entry design. *Journal of Wildlife Management,* **53,** 7–15.

Potts, G.R. 1986. *The partridge: pesticides, predation and conservation.* London: Collins.

Potts, G.R., Tapper, S.C. & Hudson, P.J. 1984. Population fluctuations in red grouse: analysis of bag records and a simulation model. *Journal of Animal Ecology,* **53,** 31–36.

Rands, M.R.W. 1988. The effect of nest site selection on nest predation in grey partridges (*Perdix perdix*) and red-legged partridges (*Alectoris rufa*). *Ornis Scandinavica,* **19,** 35–40.

Ratcliffe, D.A. 1990. *Bird life of mountain and upland.* Cambridge: Cambridge University Press.

Ratcliffe, D.A. 1993. *The peregrine falcon.* Calton: Poyser.

Redpath, C.J., Thirgood, S.J. & Redpath, S.M. 1995. Evaluation of methods to estimate field vole *Mictrotus agrestis* abundance in upland habitats. *Journal of Zoology,* **237,** 49–57.

Redpath, S.M. 1989. *The effect of hen harriers and other predators on red grouse populations in Scotland.* PhD thesis, University of Leeds.

Redpath, S.M. 1991. The impact of hen harriers on red grouse breeding success. *Journal of Applied Ecology,* **28,** 659–671.

Redpath, S.M. 1992. Behavioural interactions between hen harriers and their moorland prey. *Ornis Scandinavica,* **23,** 73–80.

Redpath, S.M., Madders, M., Donnelly, E., Anderson, B., Thirgood, S.J. & McLead, D. 1997. Nest site selection by hen harriers in Scotland. *Bird Study.* In press.

Robertson, P.A. & Rosenberg, A.A. 1988.

Harvesting gamebirds. In: *Ecology and management of gamebirds,* edited by P.J. Hudson & M.R.W. Rands, 177–201. Oxford: Blackwell Scientific.

Roseberry, J.L. 1979. Bobwhite population responses to exploitation: real and simulated. *Journal of Wildlife Management,* **43**, 285–305.

Royama, T. 1992. *Analytical population dynamics.* London: Chapman and Hall.

Savory, C.J. 1977. The food of red grouse chicks (*Lagopus lagopus scoticus*). *Ibis,* **119**, 1–9.

Schieck, J.O. 1988. *Territory selection and site fidelity in willow ptarmigan.* PhD thesis, University of Alberta.

Schipper, W.J.A., Buurma, L.S. & Bossenbroek, P.H. 1975. Comparative study of hunting behaviour of wintering hen harriers *Circus cyaneus* and marsh harriers *Circus aeruginosus. Ardea,* **63**, 1–29.

Simmons, R., Barnard, P., MacWhirter, B. & Hansen, G.L. 1986. The influence of microtines on polygyny, productivity, age and provisioning of breeding northern harriers: a five-year study. *Canadian Journal of Zoology,* **64**, 2447–2456.

Sinclair, A.R.E. 1989. Population regulation in animals. In: *Ecological concepts,* edited by J.M. Cherrett, 197–241. Oxford: Blackwell Scientific.

Solomon, M.E. 1949. The natural control of animal populations. *Journal of Animal Ecology,* **18**, 1–35.

Stenseth, N.Ch., Bjornstad, O.N. & Falck, W. 1996. Is spacing behaviour coupled with predation causing the microtine density cycle? A synthesis of current process-orientated and pattern-orientated studies. *Proceedings of the Royal Society of London,* **263B**, 1423–1435.

Stephens, D.W. & Krebs, J.R. 1987. *Foraging theory.* Princeton: Princeton University Press.

Sydes, C. & Miller, G.R. 1988. Range management and nature conservation in the British uplands. In: *Ecological change in the uplands,* edited by M.B.Usher & D.B.A. Thompson, 323–339. Oxford: Blackwell Scientific.

Tapper, S. 1992. *Game heritage. an ecological review of shooting and gamekeeping records.* Fordingbridge: The Game Conservancy Trust.

Tapper, S.C., Potts, G.R. & Brockless, M.H. 1996. The effect of experimental reductions in predator presence on the breeding success and population density of grey partridges *Perdix perdix. Journal of Applied Ecology,* **33**, 968–979.

Temeles, E.J. 1986. Reversed sexual size dimorphism: effect on resource defense and foraging behaviors of nonbreeding northern harriers. *The Auk,* **103**, 70–78.

Teerink, B.J. 1991. *Hair of west–European mammals.* Cambridge: Cambridge University Press.

Thirgood, S.J., Leckie, F.M. & Redpath, S.M. 1995. Diurnal and seasonal variation in line transect counts of moorland passerines. *Bird Study,* **42**, 257–259.

Thirgood, S.J., Redpath, S.M., Hudson, P.J., Hurley, M.H. & Aebischer, N.J. 1995. Effects of necklace radio transmitters on survival and breeding success of red grouse *Lagopus lagopus scoticus. Wildlife Biology,* **1**, 121–126.

Thirgood, S.J., Redpath, S.M., Hudson, P.J. & Donnelly, E. 1997. Estimating the cause and rate of mortality in red grouse. *Wildlife Biology.* In press.

Thompson, D.B.A., MacDonald, A.J., Marsden, J.H. & Galbraith, C.A.1995. Upland heather moorland in Great Britain: a review of international importance, vegetation change, and some objectives for nature conservation. *Biological Conservation,* **71**, 163–178.

Turchin, P. 1995. Population regulation: old arguments and a new synthesis. In: *Population dynamics – new approaches and synthesis,* edited by N. Cappuccino & P.W. Price, 19–40. San Diego: Academic Press.

Watson, A. 1985. Social class, socially-induced loss, recruitment and breeding of red grouse. *Oecologia,* **67**, 493–498.

Watson, A. & Jenkins, D. 1964. Notes on the behaviour of the red grouse. *British Birds,* **57**, 137–170.

Watson, A. & Miller, G.R. 1971. Territory size and aggression in a fluctuating red grouse population. *Journal of Animal Ecology,* **40**, 367–383.

Watson, A. & Miller, G.R. 1976. *Grouse management.* Fordingbridge: The Game Conservancy Trust.

Watson, A. & Moss, R. 1990. Spacing behaviour and winter loss in red grouse. In: *Red grouse population processes,* edited by A.N.Lance & J.H.Lawton, 35–52. Sandy, Beds: Royal Society for the Protection of Birds.

Watson, A., Moss, R., Rothery, P. & Parr, R. 1984. Demographic causes and predictive models of population fluctuation in red grouse. *Journal of Animal Ecology,* **53**, 639–662.

Watson, A., Moss, R., Parr, R., Mountford, M.D. & Rothery, P. 1994. Kin landownership, differential aggression between kin and non-kin, and population fluctuations in red grouse. *Journal of Animal Ecology,* **63**, 39–50.

Watson, D. 1977. *The hen harrier.* Berkhamsted: Poyser Press.

Weir, D. 1978. Wild peregrines and grouse. *The Falconer,* **7**, 98–102.

White, G.C. & Garrott, R.A. 1990. *Analysis of wildlife radiotracking data.* London: Academic Press.

Wikman, M. & Linden, H. 1981. The influence of food supply on goshawk population size. In: *Understanding the goshawk,* edited by R.E. Kenward & I.M. Lindsay, 105–113. Oxford: International Association for Falconry and Conservation of Birds of Prey.

Willebrand, T. 1988. *Demography and ecology of a black grouse population.* PhD thesis, Uppsala University, Sweden.

Williams, J. 1985. Statistical analysis of fluctuations in red grouse bag data. *Oecologia (Berlin),* **65**, 269–272.

Yalden, D.W. & Morris, P.A. 1990. *The analysis of owl pellets.* London: The Mammal Society.

Acknowledgements

We are grateful to the landowners for allowing us to conduct the work on their land and also the estate factors for their support over the past five years. In particular, we thank the Earl of Dalkeith and Buccleuch Estates for generously providing a home for the project and Gareth Lewis for all his help at Langholm. The work would not have been possible without the assistance and support of the gamekeepers, and we would especially like to thank Brian Mitchell and the other Langholm keepers – Raymond Gibson, Kevin Hay and Buzz McNeil – for putting up with us all throughout the project.

The work was overseen by a steering committee consisting of Mark Avery, Ian Bainbridge, Peter Buckley, Michael Clark, Charles Connell, the Earl of Dalkeith, Colin Galbraith, Rhys Green, Gareth Lewis, Stuart Housden, Peter Hudson, Brian Mitchell, David Newborn, Ian Newton, Andrew Panter, Dick Potts, Peter Reynolds, Peter Robertson and Des Thompson. All have provided useful and constructive comments on the project over the five years. In particular, the chairman Ian Newton and Dick Potts, Peter Hudson and Peter Robertson supported and encouraged us throughout the project. We are also especially grateful to Ian Newton for reading through endless drafts and for greatly improving the final product. Nicholas Aebischer and, in particular, Peter Rothery provided considerable statistical support. Mick Marquiss, Robert Moss and Adam Watson provided valuable criticisms of the work. We also thank Keith Brockie for the cover painting and the wonderful illustrations throughout the publication, and Penny Ward and Karen Goodsir for their sterling efforts in typesetting the document and redrawing many of the figures.

Numerous people helped with aspects of the work and we are greatly indebted to all of the following: Bruce Anderson, John Armitage, Miriam Baines, Graeme Buchanan, Steve Campbell, Derek Calder, Greg Carrier, Roger Clarke, Chris Coles, Jan Collins, Ciaran Cronin, Eric Donnelly, Matthew Denny, Alan Elliott, Brian Etheridge, Robin Foster, Ricki Gladwell, Isla Graham, John Halliday, John Hardy, Malcolm Henderson, Mike Henry, Chris Hill, Mac Hotson, Jan Jansen, Jean Johnson, Lars Klein, Peter Kirk, Karen Laurenson, Fiona Leckie, Pat Lindley, Mike Madders, Ann Martin, José Martinez, Roel May, Alison McKnight, Ian Miller, Pete Moore, Dave Newborn, Mike Nicholl, Jim O'Donnell, Malcolm Ogilvie, Dave Parish, Lorraine Parkinson, Hugo Rainey, Robin Reid, Chris Rollie, Kate Redpath, Dick Roxburgh, Adam Smith, Trevor Smith, Patrick Stirling-Aird, Bob Stakim, Malcolm Stott, Andy Tharme, Andrew Walton and a number of short-term volunteers. We are also grateful to Roger Clarke for careful analysis of all the harrier pellets. Our dogs, Briadh, Islay, Jet and Jura, worked harder than any of us and provided much amusement in the field.

The study was funded by the Buccleuch Estates, Peter Buckley of Westerhall Estates, the Game Conservancy Trust, the Game Conservancy Scottish Research Trust, the Institute of Terrestrial Ecology, the Joint Nature Conservation Committee, the Royal Society for the Protection of Birds and Scottish Natural Heritage. The grouse radio-tracking work was funded by a Natural Environment Research Council grant, and some of the small mammal work was funded by a grant from the British Ecological Society.

We are especially grateful to the Cuthberts, the Elliotts and the Hotsons for their friendship and kindness throughout the project and to Barbara Lewis for providing delicious food at all our steering committee meetings.

Finally, special thanks to Kate for coping so well with the constant stream of students, field assistants and visiting ecologists, and to both Karen and Kate for putting up with us.

Stephen Redpath and Simon Thirgood

Appendix 1

Scientific names of species referred to in the text

Birds

Blackbird	*Terdus merula*
Black grouse	*Tetrao tetrix*
Black-headed gull	*Larus ridibundus*
Blue tit	*Parus caeruleus*
Brambling	*Fringilla montifringilla*
Buzzard	*Buteo buteo*
Capercaillie	*Tetrao urogallus*
Carrion crow	*Corvus corone*
Chaffinch	*Fringilla coelebs*
Common gull	*Larus canus*
Common sandpiper	*Tringa hypoleucos*
Common tern	*Sterna hirundo*
Cuckoo	*Cuculus canorus*
Curlew	*Numenius arquata*
Feral/racing pigeon	*Columbia livia*
Golden eagle	*Aquila chrysaetos*
Golden plover	*Pluvialis apricaria*
Goshawk	*Accipiter gentilis*
Grey partridge	*Perdix perdix*
Hen harrier	*Circus cyaneus*
Hooded crow	*Corvus corone cornix*
Jackdaw	*Corvus monedula*
Jay	*Garrulus glandarius*
Kestrel	*Falco tinnunculus*
Lapwing	*Vanellus vanellus*
Linnet	*Acanthis cannabina*
Magpie	*Pica pica*
Mallard	*Anas platyrhynchos*
Meadow pipit	*Anthus pratensis*
Merlin	*Falco columbarius*
Mistle thrush	*Turdus viscivorus*
Oystercatcher	*Haematopus ostralegus*
Peregrine	*Falco peregrinus*
Pheasant	*Phasianus colchicus*
Pied wagtail	*Motacilla alba*
Ptarmigan	*Lagopus mutus*
Raven	*Corvus corax*
Red grouse	*Lagopus lagopus scoticus*
Red-legged partridge	*Alectoris rufa*
Redshank	*Tringa totanus*
Reed bunting	*Emberiza schoeniclus*
Ring ouzel	*Turdus torquatus*
Rook	*Corvus frugilegus*
Sedge warbler	*Acrocephalus schoenobaenus*
Short-eared owl	*Asio flammeus*
Siskin	*Carduelis spinus*
Skylark	*Alauda arvensis*
Snipe	*Gallinago gallinago*
Song thrush	*Turdus philomelos*
Sparrowhawk	*Accipiter nisus*
Starling	*Sturnus vulgaris*
Stock dove	*Columba oenas*
Stonechat	*Saxicola torquata*
Tengmalm's owl	*Aegolius funereus*
Wheatear	*Oenanthe oenanthe*
Winchat	*Saxicola rubetra*
Willow ptarmigan	*Lagopus lagopus lagopus*
Willow warbler	*Phylloscopus trochilis*
Wood pigeon	*Columba palumbus*
Wren	*Troglodytes troglodytes*

Mammals

Brown hare	*Lepus capensis*
Common shrew	*Sorex araneus*
Fox	*Vulpes vulpes*
Marten	*Martes martes*
Mole	*Talpa europaea*
Mountain hare	*Lepus timidus*
Pygmy shrew	*Sorex minutus*
Rabbit	*Oryctolagus cuniculus*
Red deer	*Cervus elaphus*
Short-tailed field vole	*Microtus agrestis*
Snow-shoe hare	*Lepus americanus*
Stoat	*Mustela erminea*
Weasel	*Mustela nivalis*
Wood/field mouse	*Apodemus sylvaticus*

Plants

Bilberry	*Vaccinium myrtilus*
Bracken	*Pteridium aquilinum*
Common rush	*Juncus effusus*
Cottongrass	*Eriophorum vaginatum*
	E. angustifolium
Heather (ling)	*Calluna vaginatum*
Bell heather	*Erica cinerea*
Cross-leaved heath	*Erica tetralix*
Purple moor grass	*Molinia caerulea*

Other

Adder	*Vipera berus*
Common lizard	*Lacerta vivipara*
Sheep tick	*Ixodes ricinus*

Appendix 2

The numbers of harrier prey items (listed alphabetically) identified to species from watches at nests at Langholm, moor B and moor E

Species	Langholm	Moor B	Moor E
Number of nests	22	2	2
Adder	1		
Blackbird	1		
Black-headed gull		1	
Brown hare	1		
Blue tit	1		
Chaffinch	1		
Cuckoo	1		
Common lizard	6		
Common shrew	8		
Curlew	16	3	
Feral pigeon		1	
Field vole	120	3	1
Golden plover	2		1
Lapwing	5		2
Merlin	2		
Mistle thrush	4		
Mountain hare	3		
Mole	1		
Meadow pipit	946	67	22
Oystercatcher		1	
Pheasant	2		15
Pied wagtail	1	2	
Rabbit	15		4
Red grouse	261		2
Reed bunting		1	
Rook	1		
Sedge warbler		1	
Skylark	102	6	15
Starling		1	
Stonechat	3		
Snipe	4		1
Songthrush	1		
Wheatear	1		
Wood mouse	1		
Wren	2		
Willow warble	1		
Winchat	2		5

Appendix 3

Estimates of grouse losses to harriers and peregrines – calculations, assumptions and tests of assumptions

---

Each section in this Appendix refers to the appropriate section in Chapter 6. Each contains details of relevant calculations, followed by a list of assumptions (in bold) and a discussion of any supporting evidence for those assumptions.

HARRIERS

Harrier predation on grouse during the breeding season

The numbers of grouse chicks removed by harriers in each year at Langholm was estimated over four periods of the harrier breeding season: incubation, early nestling, late nestling and post-fledging.

Estimates from all four periods assume that:
1. **watches from hides at nests gave a true representation of provisioning at those nests;**
2. **nests watched were representative of all harrier nests at Langholm;**
3. **no predation on grouse occurred by non-breeding harriers, or by breeders following failure.**

1. Most female harriers appeared to be relatively unaffected by the hides, and returned to their nests within a few minutes after being disturbed. However, over the four years a small number of females alarm-called whenever an observer was in the hide. For these females, watches were abandoned after two or three attempts. These data were excluded from further analysis.
2. Nest watches were conducted on the same part of Langholm moor in each year. We did, however, collect harrier pellets from other nests on other parts of the moor. We compared the percentage of pellets containing grouse between nests which were watched and those not watched: watched: N=14, mean=24.5%; not watched N=7, mean=19.2%; $F_{1,19}$=0.43, P=0.52. Thus, these data suggested that, at least in terms of the percentage of pellets that contained grouse, nests watched were representative of all nests at Langholm. Bigamous harriers took more grouse chicks than monogamous ones during the breeding season. However, because of small sample sizes, we have not taken this into account in our calculations. We tried to be representative in our choice of nests, but a comparison of ratios of bigamous/monogamous birds watched to the ratio present on the moor as a whole suggested that our figures may have slightly overestimated the true value of grouse chick losses in 1994 and underestimated it in 1996. In the other years the birds watched were representative in terms of mating status.
3. Failed breeders and non-breeders almost certainly took some grouse chicks. However, we suspected that predation by these individuals was negligible, because failed breeders (some of which were tagged), which did not relay, appeared to move off the study area within a few days and were not seen again. Similarly, most yearling birds which were present and displaying in the spring, but which did not subsequently nest, had left the moor by the time the grouse chicks hatched in late May.

Incubation

For those males whose young hatched after 28 May, we estimated the extent of grouse removal in any one year before hatching using the equation outlined below.

Numbers of grouse chicks removed (incubation) = days x hours x rate x %grouse

where:

days = total number of days females incubated after 28 May
hours = 15 hours hunting per day
rate = 0.51 items per hour
% grouse = % of grouse in diet of males with chicks over same period (28 May–3 July).

Results were as follows.

	1992	1993	1994	1995	1996
Nests hatched after 28 May	0	3	8	4	5
Total days	0	60	50	12	42
Hours	0	900	750	180	630
% grouse	–	6.87	14.44	10.50	5.55
Nos of grouse	0	31.5	55.2	9.6	17.8

Additional assumption
The prey of males with chicks was the same as those with eggs.

This assumption was tested using data collected in Perthshire in 1988 (Redpath 1989). Here, 39 prey items were identified from nests with eggs (by watching where females ate the prey and later checking that site for remains), and 94 items were identified from nests with chicks over the same period. The proportion of grouse in the diet was not significantly different between the egg and chick stages (36% for males with eggs vs 39% for males with chicks; $G=0.06$, 2 df, NS).

Early nestling period

In each year, the number of grouse removed by males and females over this period was estimated using the following equation:

> Numbers of grouse chicks removed = days x hours x rate x number
> where:
>> days = 28 (4 weeks x 7 days)
>> hours = 15 hours hunting per day
>> rate = average number of grouse brought to nests per hour (data in Table 6.1)
>> number = number of breeding male and female harriers.

Results were as follows.

	1993	1994	1995	1996
Male harriers				
Grouse per hour	0.041±0.015	0.100±0.014	0.106±0.033	0.051±0.020
Grouse chicks per male	17.22	42.00	44.52	21.42
Nos of successful males	4	6	6	7
Total grouse taken by males	68.9±25.2	252.0±35.3	267.1±83.2	149.9±58.8
Female harriers				
Grouse per hour	0.054±0.010	0.080±0.018	0.070±0.016	0.056±0.022
Grouse chicks per female	22.68	33.60	29.40	23.52
Nos of successful females	4	9	8	12
Total grouse taken by females	90.7±16.8	302.4±68.0	235.2±53.8	282.2±110.9
Total grouse removed (early nestling period)	159.6±30.3	554.4±76.6	502.3±99.1	432.2±125.5

Additional assumption
All grouse chicks were correctly identified at the nest.

Grouse chicks could be easily distinguished from hides, by the distinctive golden plumage and feathered feet. We may have misidentified some black grouse as red grouse chicks, but these birds were rare and were never knowingly found as prey remains at Langholm.

Late nestling period

Because prey identification from the hides became increasingly difficult after week 4, we assessed the number of grouse taken by each bird using the proportion of grouse in the male and female diet from weeks 3 and 4 (samples were too small in week 4 alone) multiplied by the provisioning rates for weeks 5–6.

> Numbers of grouse chicks removed = days x hours x rate x number
> where:
>> days = 14 (2 weeks x 7 days)
>> hours = 15 hours hunting per day
>> rate = average number of grouse brought to nests per hour; this was based on the overall provisioning rate in the late nestling period) x % of grouse in the diet during 3rd and 4th week of nestling period 1
>> number = number of breeding male and female harriers.

Results were as follows.

	1993	1994	1995	1996
Male harriers				
Grouse per hour	0.028±0.005	0.081±0.005	0.024±0.011	0.021±0.007
Grouse chicks per male	5.88	17.01	5.04	4.41
Nos of successful males	4	6	6	7
Total grouse removed by males	23.5±4.2	102.1±6.3	30.2±13.8	30.9±10.2

continued on next page

Female harriers

Grouse per hour	0.072±0.010	0.067±0.030	0.117±0.043	0.075±0.021
Grouse chicks per female	15.2	14.10	24.52	15.83
Nos of successful females	4	9	8	12
Total grouse removed by females	60.5±9.0	126.6±57.7	196.6±72.7	189.0±54.3
Total grouse removed (late nestling period)	84.0±9.9	228.7±58.0	226.8±74.0	219.9±55.2

Additional assumption

The percentage of grouse in the male and female diet in the late nestling period was the same as the percentage in the third and fourth week of the early nestling period.

For tests of these assumptions see Chapter 6 – Post-fledging period.

Post-fledging period

For this period, we assessed predation rates by multiplying the provisioning rate by the percentage of grouse in the diet, in the 3rd and 4th weeks of the early nestling period. In the absence of a measure of provisioning in this period in 1993 and 1996, for these two years we used the average provisioning rates for 1994 and 1995.

Numbers of grouse chicks removed (post-fledging) = days x hours x rate x number

where:

days = 18 days (fledging to dispersal)
hours = 15 hours hunting per day
rate = average number of grouse brought to nests per hour; this was based on the overall provisioning rate during the post-fledging period x % of grouse in the diet during the third and fourth week
number = number of breeding male and female harriers.

Results were as follows.

	1993	1994	1995	1996
Male harriers				
Grouse per hour	0.007	0.016±0.016	0.004	0.008
Grouse chicks per male	1.83	4.38	0.99	2.22
Nos of successful males	4	6	6	7
Total grouse removed by males	7.3	26.3±26.3	5.9	15.5
Female harriers				
Grouse per hour	0.070	0.128±0.047	0.178±0.137	0.148
Grouse chicks per female	18.87	34.65	48.05	40.07
Nos of successful females	4	9	8	12
Total grouse removed by females	75.5	311.8±114.2	384.4±295.9	480.8
Total grouse removed (post-fledging)	82.8	338.1±117.2	390.3	496.3

Additional assumptions

1. **The percentage of grouse in male and female diet in the post-fledging period was the same as the percentage in third and fourth week of the early nestling period.**
2. **The provisioning rate (post-fledging) in 1993 and 1996 was the same as in 1994 and 1995.**
3. **There was no additional predation by harrier chicks.**

1. To test the assumption that the percentage of grouse in the diet remained the same through all three periods, we examined pellets collected around nest sites through the breeding seasons of 1993–96. We excluded samples of less than ten pellets and compared the percentage of pellets containing grouse in weeks 1–4 (N=7 nests, mean=24.9%), 5–6 (N=9 nests, mean=23.9%) and 7–dispersal (N=7 nests, mean=28.8%). Removing the statistical effects of year, the collection period had no significant effect on the proportion of pellets containing grouse ($F_{1,18}$=0.75, P=0.4). These data support the assumption that the percentage of grouse in the diet remained the same through all three periods.
2. We have no data to test this assumption in this period. However, a comparison of provisioning rates between 1993, 1996 and 1994–95 in weeks 5+6, revealed significant differences for both males ($F_{2,10}$=4.2, P=0.05) and females ($F_{2,17}$=3.7, P=0.04), with provisioning rates being highest in 1993 and 1996 in both sexes. If this pattern held over the following two weeks, grouse chick loss would have been underestimated in 1993 and 1996.
3. Once fledged, young harriers may also have killed some grouse chicks before dispersing. However, observations during the period from week 7–dispersal suggested that they depended on their parents, and were rarely successful at catching prey. Of 42 observed strikes at prey, only three were successful (all on small mammals). No strikes by young harriers at grouse were observed.

Total numbers of grouse chicks removed by harriers

Standard errors for estimates of grouse chick losses to harriers were determined for each sex in each year, using the following equation:

$$\text{Standard error} = \sqrt{\sum_{i=1}^{i=n} N_i^2 t_i^2 \, \frac{s_i^2}{n_i^2}}$$

where:

   i = period 1 (early nestling period) to 3 (post-fledging period)
   N = number of nests on moor
   n = number of nests observed
   t = time available for hunting
   s = sample variance.

The standard error for the total estimate was derived as follows.

$$\text{SE (total)} = \sqrt{\text{SE}^2\,(\text{male}) + \text{SE}^2\,(\text{female})}$$

95% confidence limits were determined as the standard error x 1.96.

Losses from 1 April to 17 July

From the 29 May (harrier median hatch date), there were 49 days before 17 July, when the grouse counts were conducted. The number of days from hatch to dispersal for hen harriers was approximately 60 days (Chapter 6 – Late nestling period), so grouse chick losses continued after the grouse counts. For each sex, in each period, in each year, we estimated the number of grouse chicks that harriers removed before 17 July as follows.

   Number of grouse chicks removed before 17 July = days x hours x rate
   where:
      days = number of days harriers present with young before 17 July
      hours = number of hours available for hunting (15)
      rate = average number of grouse brought to harrier nests per hour in each period

For bigamous males, the number of days in each period was determined as the average number of days spent provisioning α and β females. Results were as follows.

		1993	1994	1995	1996
Male harriers					
Incubation	Number of grouse	31.5	55.2	9.6	17.8
Early nestling	Days	103	168	168	189
period	Provisioning rate	0.041	0.10	0.106	0.051
	Number of grouse	63.3	252.0	267.1	144.6
Late nestling	Days	35	76	84	78
period	Provisioning rate	0.028	0.081	0.024	0.021
	Number of grouse	14.7	92.3	30.2	24.6
Post-fledging	Days	23	28	50	53
period	Provisioning rate	0.007	0.016	0.004	0.008
	Number of grouse	2.4	6.7	3.0	6.4
	Grouse to males	111.9	406.2	309.9	193.4
Female harriers					
Early nestling	Days	103	252	224	321
period	Provisioning rate	0.054	0.08	0.07	0.056
	Number of grouse	83.4	302.4	235.2	269.6
Late nestling	Days	35	116	112	128
period	Provisioning rate	0.072	0.067	0.117	0.075
	Number of grouse	37.8	116.6	196.6	144.0
Post-fledging	Days	23	48	71	89
period	Provisioning rate	0.070	0.128	0.178	0.148
	Number of grouse	24.1	92.2	189.6	197.6
	Grouse to females	145.3	511.2	621.4	611.2
Total grouse removed before 17 July		257.2	917.4	931.3	804.6

To estimate the number of grouse chicks taken per 0.5 km² at Langholm, we assumed that there was 41.45 km² of available grouse habitat over which the harriers hunted (Chapter 2). This estimate excluded moorland with less than 30% heather cover where grouse were likely to occur at low density. Consequently, measures of chick loss per unit area may have been slightly high. The whole grouse moor was 48.58 km² and, if this measure was used, estimates per 0.5 km² would be reduced by approximately 14%. In addition, some heather moorland occurred to the west of the estate and some grouse chicks may have been removed from there. However, up to 1996, these areas were more than 7 km from the nearest harrier nest, so the extent of any predation out of the study moor in these years was likely to have been small. In 1996 the nearest nest was 6 km from the neighbouring moorland, which in turn contained two extra harrier nests within 1 km of the study moor. In 1996 it was likely, therefore, that the number of grouse chicks removed from the study moor was underestimated.

PEREGRINES

Peregrine predation on grouse during the breeding season

To estimate the numbers of grouse removed by peregrines, we divided the breeding season into three: incubation, nestling and post-fledging periods. For each of these periods we estimated the number of grouse taken by successful and unsuccessful breeders, based on estimates of biomass requirements and a measure of the percentage of grouse in the diet at each eyrie.

Biomass requirements

The watches at peregrine nests indicated that on average 74.5 g of food arrived at the nests every hour. Assuming a 15-hour day for hunting, this gave 1118 g per day. As the nests varied in the number of chicks they contained, we used the difference in biomass to estimate the amount required by an individual chick. At site Di there were three chicks, taking an average of 69.6 g prey per h; at Lo, 84.4 g prey per h were taken, a difference of 14.8 g per h, or 222 g per day. Therefore we could estimate that an adult required 12.6 g per hour, or 188 g per day.

Assumptions

1. **Prey remains and food requirements from hides gave an accurate representation of grouse killed.**
2. **Estimates of food requirements from watches at nests gave an accurate representation for all nests over 42 days.**
3. **At each nest there were no differences between years in the percentage of grouse in the diet.**

1. As discussed in Chapter 2, prey remains were likely to have overestimated larger prey, as small items were often completely consumed. However, pellet and prey remains gave similar estimates of the percentage of grouse in the diet of peregrines during the summer, and a comparison of estimates of the percentage of grouse by biomass during the three nest watches (32% from hides and 21% of 105 prey remains) indicated that prey remains may have slightly underestimated the percentage of grouse in the diet.
2. With such a small number of nests watched, it was difficult to say how representative the watches from hides were in terms of biomass requirements. However, Weir (1978) stated that peregrine chicks required up to 300 g of prey per day, depending on their age, whereas an adult required 175 g. Ratcliffe (1993) estimated that an adult peregrine required approximately 159 g of prey per day. These figures suggested that our estimates of 222 g per day for a chick and 188 g per day for the adults were of the right order.
3. A comparison of the percentage of grouse in the prey remains found at eyries over years, based on Table 6.4, indicated that differences between years were not significant, excluding years when less than ten prey items were recovered, and controlling for site, $F_{1,7}=0.02$, P=0.88. However, sample sizes, and therefore the power to detect differences, were small.

Incubation

During the pre-hatch period of 40 days, we estimated that each adult peregrine on territory required 7.5 kg of prey (40 days x 188 g per day). An estimate of the number of grouse removed per pair was determined as follows:

> Biomass requirements = 188 g x 2 adults x 40 days = 15.04 kg
> Number of grouse removed = (biomass requirements x % grouse)/637 g per grouse
> where:
> > % grouse = % grouse (by biomass) in prey remains at each eyrie
> > 637 g = average weight of grouse during spring.

Results were as follows.

	Number of pairs	Site	% grouse	Incubation	Total grouse taken
1992	3	St	1.8	0.4	
		Di	19.3	4.5	10.1
		Ms	22.0	5.2	
1993	3	St	1.8	0.4	
		Di	19.3	4.5	10.1
		Ms	22.0	5.2	
1994	6	St	1.8	0.4	
		Di	19.3	4.5	
		Ms	22.0	5.2	
		So	19.2	4.5	24.5
		Lo	26.5	6.3	
		Rf	15.5	3.6	
1995	6	St	1.8	0.4	
		Di	19.3	4.5	
		Ms	22.0	5.2	
		So	19.2	4.5	24.5
		Lo	26.5	6.3	
		Rf	15.5	3.6	
1996	5	St	1.8	0.4	
		Di	19.3	4.5	
		Ms	22.0	5.2	20.9
		So	19.2	4.5	
		Lo	26.5	6.3	

Additional assumption

Adult food requirements and diet were the same during incubation as during the nestling stage.

Overall, data from six eyries around Langholm (years pooled) indicated that more pellets contained grouse in the spring (26.1%±5%) than in the summer (15.5%±1%), although the difference was not significant (t=0.93, 5 df, P=0.2). For the purposes of this analysis, we therefore assumed, conservatively, that the proportion of grouse in the diet remained constant.

Nestling period

This period was taken as 42 days, when estimates of the number of grouse taken to each eyrie were made using the following equation:

Biomass requirements = (2 adults x 188 g x 42 days) + (no. chicks x 222 g x 42 days)

Number grouse removed = (biomass requirements x % grouse)/607 g

where:

% grouse = % grouse (by biomass) in prey remains at each eyrie

607 g = average weight of grouse during summer.

Results were as follows.

Year	Number of nests	Site	Chicks	Grouse (%)	Biomass requirements (kg)	Number of grouse taken	Total grouse taken
1992	3	St	2	1.8	34.4	1.0	
		Di	0	19.3	15.8	5.0	11.7
		Ms	0	22.0	15.8	5.7	
1993	3	St	3	1.8	43.8	1.3	
		Di	0	19.3	15.8	5.0	12.0
		Ms	0	22.0	15.8	5.7	
1994	6	St	3	1.8	43.8	1.3	
		Di	3	19.3	43.8	14.0	
		Ms	0	22.0	15.8	5.7	
		So	0	19.2	15.8	5.0	36.9
		Lo	0	26.5	15.8	6.9	
		Rf	0	15.5	15.8	4.0	
1995	6	St	4	1.8	53.1	1.6	
		Di	3	19.3	43.9	14.0	
		Ms	0	22.0	15.8	5.7	43.1
		So	2	19.2	34.4	10.9	
		Lo	0	26.5	15.8	6.9	
		Rf	0	15.5	15.8	4.0	
1996	5	St	1	1.8	25.1	0.7	
		Di	3	19.3	43.8	14.0	
		Ms	2	22.0	34.4	12.5	67.2
		So	4	19.2	53.1	16.8	
		Lo	4	26.5	53.1	23.2	

Post-fledging period

The period of fledging to dispersal was taken as 60 days. In this time the food requirements of chicks and adults were assumed to be equal. The number of grouse removed was estimated as:

Biomass requirements (post-fledge) = 188 g x number of peregrines (2 adults + n chicks) x 60 days

Number of grouse removed = (biomass requirements x % grouse)/607 g

where:

% grouse = % grouse (by biomass) in prey remains at each eyrie

607 g = average weight of grouse during summer.

Results were as follows.

Year	Number of nests	Site	Chicks	Grouse (%)	Biomass requirements (kg)	Number of grouse taken	Total grouse taken
1992	3	St	2	1.8	45.1	1.3	
		Di	0	19.3	22.6	7.2	16.7
		Ms	0	22.0	22.6	8.2	
1993	3	St	3	1.8	56.4	1.6	
		Di	0	19.3	22.6	7.2	17.0
		Ms	0	22.0	22.6	8.2	
1994	6	St	3	1.8	56.4	1.6	
		Di	3	19.3	56.4	17.9	
		Ms	0	22.0	22.6	8.2	
		So	0	19.2	22.6	7.1	50.4
		Lo	0	26.5	22.6	9.8	
		Rf	0	15.5	22.6	5.8	
1995	6	St	4	1.8	67.7	2.1	
		Di	3	19.3	56.4	17.9	
		Ms	0	22.0	22.6	8.2	
		So	2	19.2	45.1	14.3	58.1
		Lo	0	26.5	22.6	9.8	
		Rf	0	15.5	22.6	5.8	
1996	5	St	1	1.8	33.8	1.0	
		Di	3	19.3	56.4	17.9	
		Ms	2	22.0	45.1	16.3	86.1
		So	4	19.2	67.7	21.4	
		Lo	4	26.5	67.7	29.5	

Additional assumptions

1. Diet of breeding peregrines and failed breeders were the same.

2. The percentage of grouse in the diet was the same during the nestling and post-fledging periods.

We were unable to collect much prey material from failed breeders and, similarly, most prey from successful breeders were collected prior to fledging, so we could not test the validity of these assumptions.

Losses between grouse counts

For the purpose of these calculations, no broods would have dispersed before 17 July, when the grouse counts were conducted. So, given the median hatch date of 10 May, this would give 26 days from fledging to the grouse counts. We therefore recalculated post-fledging losses to peregrines over 26 days, using the same equations as in Chapter 6 – Post-fledging period. These estimates were then added to those derived during the incubation (Chapter 6 – Incubation) and nestling periods (Chapter 6 – Nestling period).

Printed in the United Kingdom for the
Stationery Office
J26605 C10 10/97 (9091)